CONTROL SYSTEM
DOCUMENTATION

Applying Symbols and Identification **2nd Edition**

CONTROL SYSTEM DOCUMENTATION

Applying Symbols and Identification **2nd Edition**

by Thomas McAvinew and Raymond Mulley

Notice
The information presented in this publication is for the general education of the reader. Because neither the author nor the publisher have any control over the use of the information by the reader, both the author and the publisher disclaim any and all liability of any kind arising out of such use. The reader is expected to exercise sound professional judgment in using any of the information presented in a particular application.

Additionally, neither the author nor the publisher have investigated or considered the affect of any patents on the ability of the reader to use any of the information in a particular application. The reader is responsible for reviewing any possible patents that may affect any particular use of the information presented.

Any references to commercial products in the work are cited as examples only. Neither the author nor the publisher endorses any referenced commercial product. Any trademarks or trade names referenced belong to the respective owner of the mark or name. Neither the author nor the publisher makes any representation regarding the availability of any referenced commercial product at any time. The manufacturer's instructions on use of any commercial product must be followed at all times, even if in conflict with the information in this publication.

Copyright © 2004 ISA – The Instrumentation, Systems, and Automation Society

Printed in the United States of America.
10 9 8 7 6 5 4 3

ISBN-10: 1-55617-896-4 (pbk.)
ISBN-13: 978-1-55617-896-2 (pbk.)

ISA 67 Alexander Drive
P.O. Box 12277 Research Triangle Park, NC 27709

Library of Congress Cataloging-in-Publication Data

Mulley, Raymond.
Control system documentation : applying symbols and identification /
by Raymond Mulley and Thomas McAvinew.-- 2nd ed.
p. cm.
Includes index.
ISBN 1-55617-896-4 (pbk.)
1. Automatic control--Documentation. I. McAvinew, Thomas. II. Title.
TJ213.M745 2004
629.8--dc22
2004013086

Contents

Illustrations

Preface

People interested in the subject of instrumentation come from extremely diverse backgrounds. In fact, the titles "Control Systems Engineer, (CSE)" "Instrumentation and Control (I&C) Engineer," "Instrument Engineer" and "Automation Engineer" all mean slightly different things to different people. They are, however, all related. The use of "Control Systems Engineer" in this book reflects the authors' backgrounds. The title should be taken in its broadest possible sense.

Furthermore, not only engineers are interested in instrumentation, but also designers, operators, technicians, procurement people, and a host of others. When these people communicate about instrumentation, they have one common means of expression. In the exercise of their various and varied functions, they make use of symbols and identification codes as tools of communicating particular information for dedicated purposes. Further, they use these same graphic tools, often in simplified form, to help conceptualize initial engineering ideas. These tools are essential to the creative process, to the logical development of measurement and control concepts, and to the communication of these concepts to others.

The symbols and identification associated with instrumentation are not limited simply to those symbols and that identification which describe instruments and instrument functions; that which is controlled and monitored must also be symbolized and identified if the communication of information is to be complete. The symbols and identification in this book could be described, therefore, as being instrumentation-related, for, in addition to instrumentation symbols and identification methods that are easily recognized as being in the domain of control systems professionals, examples of related piping, electrical, and process symbols and identification are also included.

This book is motivated by the fundamental desire to help any interested person find the tools of communication that are necessary to the execution of his or her instrumentation-related work. Its purpose is to bring together in one place most of the symbols and identifiers that are related to instrumentation, to subject them to objectively critical review, and to give practical examples of their application.

Instrument symbols and identifiers are found on the backs of envelopes, on blackboards, in textbooks, on engineers' and designers' sketches, on flow sheets, on installation drawings, on location drawings, on loop diagrams, on logic diagrams, on wiring diagrams, in procurement documents, in start-up and operating manuals, and on piping isometric drawings, to name but a few of the documents, formal and informal, that serve as the last repositories of the products of the conceptualizing process. Since the symbols and identifiers cannot be separated from the document on which they are drawn or printed, the type of document serves as a natural basis for classification.

Indeed, this classification by type of document matches the evolutionary process that starts with the concept and then passes through preliminary design, detailed design, procurement, installation, configuration/programming, checkout, start-up, and finally, operation (with some troubleshooting thrown in for good measure). The chapter organization of this book, then attempts to follow both the natural work breakdown structure and the evolutionary sequence of control systems engineering and design work. This edition has been updated and clarified in several ways. However, the material is still presented with a perspective of functionality, rather that with an eye towards how these documents are generated. While in fact an array of evolving PC-based software systems, both commercial and "home-grown," are in use by practitioners, the authors strongly feel that a thorough understanding of the "why and what" of complete documentation packages is more important than the "how".

Although the basis for classification is by type of document, the book is primarily about symbols and identifiers. This distinction must be drawn since the actual documents are highly company-specific in content, format, and appearance, and, therefore, tend to be a bit controversial. It is the intent of the authors to help people communicate through the use of symbols and identifiers—not to dictate what formal documentation to use. It is understood that today most software-based control systems feature vendor specific self-documentation. This documentation should be considered as an adjunct to, not a substitute for, good, basic engineering firm or client-generated design documents.

It is hoped that the book will contribute in a practical way to the improvement of symbolic representation and identification in the execution of control systems engineering and design work. Further, it is hoped that it will help improve and strengthen communications among not only instrument people but all interested professionals.

About the Authors

Raymond Mulley

Ray was the original author of *Control System Documentation-Applying Symbols and Identification*. He joined ISA in 1973 and was the Chairman of SP 5.1, the committee that developed the 1984 revision of ANSI/ISA 5.1, *Instrumentation Symbols and Identification*, which was subsequently re-affirmed in 1992 and is currently undergoing a major revision once again. He is presently retired, but his new book, "Flow of Industrial Fluids — Theory and Equations," was recently published by ISA.

His over thirty years of professional experience was obtained while working for Fluor Daniel (Mississauga, Ontario, Rochester, New York and Irvine, California), Dravo Chemplants (Pittsburgh, Pennsylvania) and International Nickle (Sudbury, Ontario). Part of this experience was in private practice as a professional engineer in the field of process hazards analysis and control. His experience ranges from start-up engineer to instrument and electrical supervisor, instrument design engineer, chief instrument engineer, director of design engineering and hazards analyst.

Thomas C. McAvinew

Joining Ray in this second edition, Tom has nearly forty years of experience in various instrumentation positions with several operating and engineering firms. A 1963 Chemical Engineering graduate of Lowell Technological Institute (now the University of Massachusetts-Lowell), he transitioned to the field of instrumentation and control under the tutelage of Marvin D. Weiss and William J. Baker at Uniroyal Chemical facilities in Naugatuck, Connecticut and Baton Rouge, Louisiana respectively. In 1997 he formed Instrumentation and Control Engineering, LLC, under which he provided expert testimony and consulting, and Y2K auditing and remediation services. He is a registered Professional Engineer in Colorado having passed the first NCEES administered Control Systems exam in 1992.

He joined ISA in 1964 and became active in control system documentation standards while a member of the Lehigh Valley Section from 1978-1983. His work on several ISA SP 5 committees led to an appointment to the S&P Department Board as a Managing Director, responsible for the SP 5 committees, and to the Publication Department Board as Liaison Director for S&P. He has been a member of the Denver Section since 1984 and has held several elected positions including three terms as Section President and is a former District 8 Vice President.

He is an ISA Life Senior member and a Senior Control Systems Engineer with the Jacobs Engineering Group in Golden, Colorado.

THE TOOLS OF COMMUNICATION

▨ INTRODUCTION: SYMBOLS AND IDENTIFICATION

This chapter establishes a philosophical and practical basis for symbolism and for identification methods. No graphic examples are given—deliberately. Sound understanding, by necessity, precedes rational application

The What and the Why

In control engineering and design work, symbols and identifiers are used as graphical representations of concepts, ideas about things (devices), or functions (actions performed by devices). These symbols and identifiers are used for two fundamental purposes:

1. To help in the conceptualizing process
2. To help with the communication of information

Conception and communication are the two major categories of the study of symbols and identification; other categories are all subsets of these two. For instance, recording information for future use is nothing more than postponed communication. Indeed, it could be argued that conceptualization is a form of self-communication and that, therefore, there is only one category—communication. However, there tends to be a quantum difference in the detail used in sketches that are intended to help the conceptualization process and drawings that are used for purposes of formal communication, so there is a practical basis for considering two major categories.

Why use symbols? Symbols are a shorthand representation of a great deal of detail that otherwise would require pages of description. They do not stand alone. They appear on various drawings such as flowsheets, loop diagrams, and installation details; and they are supported, necessarily, by other documents such as instrument indexes and data sheets. They serve a particular purpose; to convey the idea that a device or function exists and that it has definite physical and functional relationships with other devices and functions and with the process being measured or controlled.

In a sense, symbols and identification methods may be likened to a language, a higher (in the computer science use of the word) language, but one that is not so structured as FORTRAN or BASIC.

The Who

When writing a book or preparing a speech, the author must keep the audience clearly in mind for the book or speech to be effectively communicated. Similarly, when an engineering document is created, along with its symbols and identification, the end users must be kept clearly in mind at all times. Learning what the end user requires to help do the job facilitates the design process. An agreed to scope of work that not only tells what is to be done but what is not to be done is most critical.

The end users of instrumentation symbols and identification are quite varied. Examples are process engineers, control systems engineers and designers; piping, electrical, and mechanical engineers; purchasing, expediting, and inspection personnel; vendor and fabricator personnel; installers, and calibration and checkout people, maintenance personnel; safety engineers; and programmers.

It is not always necessary to create a different document for each of the above categories of interested people; but it is wise to analyze which among them are likely to be users of a particular document before work is begun on it. The communication will be much more effective.

The How

It is also wise to remember that *concepts* are being communicated—not pictures. A Circle with a line across it with FIC 100 inscribed in the circle immediately indicates a discrete, panel-mounted flow controller. The fact that the device is not circular at all does not matter. The same applies to drawing a single signal line symbol to represent a signal that is transmitted on two wires. The primary concern is that information in the form of a signal is being transmitted, not that it requires two wires. Later, when it is necessary to know what terminal numbers are used, two wires will be drawn (but on a specific document and only at the terminations).

The best symbol to use is the simplest one that will get the concept across to the intended audience without leaving a sense of uneasiness that something is missing or different. At the other extreme, the reader may be left with a sense of annoyance that there is too much detail, too much clutter involved in the use of symbols. Discomfort in the minds of the audience will impede transmission of the message.

As with all methods of communication, it is first necessary to have something to say and then someone to say it to. In other words, first one must have a purpose for communication something, then the needs of the intended audience must be considered. These two factors usually will decide the type of document to be used and the degree of detail necessary to convey the message. The choice of specific symbols usually comes down to application of the correct standard. The overall impact depends largely on experience and on a sense of aesthetics.

▧ SYMBOLS, IDENTIFICATION, AND DOCUMENTATION

Both symbols and identifiers can represent hardware (a discrete, uniquely identifiable device) and the functions performed by such a device. The degree of detail involved in this representation depends on the end use of the symbols and identification. It can range from extremely simple representations to very complicated ones. For instance, a process flow diagram might indicate only that a variable is to be controlled, while the associated loop diagram would show all the devices in the control loop, their interconnections, and their locations.

Since symbols and identifiers are graphical tools, they are always found on a surface that is capable of supporting a graphic image. This surface is usually paper, but it is often a hard surface such as a blackboard. More and more frequently it is an electronic medium, for instance, a video display unit. In a broad sense, these media may all be classified as documents, since they are used to convey information.

As a document is designed, with the end user (the audience) in mind, the type of symbols and identification and the degree of detail to be used on a given document must also be chosen with the end user in mind. At times it is difficult to decide how much detail to put on a particular document. Most will err on the side of excessive detail, but this can be avoided. One golden rule is not to put the same piece of data in more than one document (or database), especially if the document is likely to be revised.

Continuity of Concept

In engineering and design work, it is normal to proceed from the general to the specific: a general concept, sketches, more detailed flowsheets, narrative specifications, individual data sheets, and so on. A continuity of concept exists throughout the various stages of the design process. The scaffolding must be erected before the building can be built.

This continuity is evident in degrees of detail: the same concept, the same device or function, but at different levels of immediate concern. The different degrees of detail are usually represented by different documents: process flow diagrams, piping and instrument diagrams, loop diagrams, installation details, etc. When going from one level or document to another, it is best not to change a symbol for the same concept radically, as doing so will cause unnecessary discomfort in the minds of most users and will inhibit communication and understanding.

For instance, going from a circular symbol to a square one for the same device simply because it is being depicted on a loop diagram instead of a flow diagram is an unnecessary abrupt transition. It forces memorization of more than one symbol for the same object. The use of a basic symbol and the addition of a terminal strip makes use of continuity of concept and is much more comforting to the thought process; or, at least, it does not cause the irritation that inhibits acceptance of the concepts being portrayed.

Communication Requires a Common Language

Common standard symbols and identifiers are not necessarily required for the conceptualizing process or for recording information for personal use. Any individual may try to live in a vacuum if he or she so chooses. However, a common means of communication is required if one wishes to exchange information with others. Communication is not possible without a common language.

The communication function takes precedence over the conceptualizing function in deciding what symbols and identifiers should be used in a particular situation. The communication function, by its nature, requires a common system. Furthermore, since we wish to communicate our ideas clearly to others and we wish not to be misunderstood, nor to misunderstand, it is inadvisable to invent our own symbols and identifiers when commonly accepted ones are readily available.

The goals of a good communications system should be simplicity, clarity, consistency, completeness, flexibility, and compactness. Judgment is involved since some of these goals may be in apparent conflict.

ISA Standards as the Prime Source

The sources of these commonly accepted symbols and identification methods are usually some form of standard: company, institutional, national, or international. Most of these standards are based, even if somewhat loosely, on the ISA 5 series of standards—even the international ones. The popularity of ISA methods may be attributed, at least in part, to the manner in which ISA standards are developed. Committees, whose members are representative of the users of the standard, develop draft standards that are subjected to public review and comment. These draft standards are revised in light of the comments and recycled until a consensus (substantial agreement) is achieved. They then are subjected to a review by ISA's Standards and Practices Board to ensure that correct procedures have been followed and that the committees that developed the drafts were indeed representative and unbiased. These methods ensure that an ISA standard will have reasonable acceptance among users. They also ensure that the "language" used will be a common one.

Symbols and Identification for Equipment and Piping

This book follows ISA standards as closely as possible. It does add many symbols and identification methods that are not usually thought of as being in the domain of instrumentation, for example, process equipment and piping symbols and identification.

However, instrument people cannot perform their work in isolation from the processes and equipment they are attempting to control, and this fact alone justifies the inclusion of symbols and identifiers for other than what is commonly recognized as being in the field of instrumentation.

Symbols, Identifiers, and Words

Although this is a book about symbols and identification methods, the judicious use of words must not be neglected. The combination of a symbol, an identifier, and a well-chosen word or two can often result in a simpler, more readily understood depiction of a complex scheme than words alone or symbols and identifiers alone. The symbol and its associated identifiers supply the general category to which the device belongs; the words supply the qualifier that specifies the device.

▨ SUMMARY

In control systems work, symbols and identifiers are basically tools of communication that graphically represent devices, functions, and their interconnections. In addition to being tools of direct communication, they help in conceptualizing and recording information about instrument systems.

These tools of communication are of interest to a wide variety of technically oriented people. The end use to which these people wish to put the graphical representations of concepts must be kept clearly in mind if the communication is to be successful. Concepts, not images, are the subject of the communication process; and concepts, not images, are the base of the most successful (most accepted) standards. Simplicity helps.

It is necessary to know what one wishes to communicate and to whom. The choice of document, the degree of detail, and the standard symbols and identification to be used then follow, usually as a matter of course.

Symbols and identifiers may represent both hardware and software functions. The degree of detail used to represent these functions depends on the purpose of the communicator and on the needs of the intended audience.

The choice of documentation follows and can range from very simple conceptual sketches to highly detailed systems diagrams and loop diagrams. Moving from one type of document to another should entail a modification of the symbols and identifiers used, not a radical change in them.

Since the principal use of symbols and identifiers is found in communication with others, common standards are needed. ISA standards, in general, have earned their place as the prime international source of symbols and identification methods.

This is primarily a book about the application of instrumentation symbols and identification. For completeness, however, related piping, electrical, and equipment symbols are included.

Finally, the use of a few well-chosen words on a drawing should not be neglected. The combination of a symbol, an identifier, and one or two judiciously selected words can communicate a concept more explicitly and more clearly than symbols, identifiers, or words alone.

▓ QUESTIONS

1. What does the chapter define as the two major categories of the study of symbols and identification?

2. Why are symbols used?

3. Who are the end users of symbols and identification? Why should they be kept in mind?

4. What is it that is being communicated, pictures or concepts?

5. Why is it important to consider the impact of the symbols on the end user?

6. Can symbols represent both hardware and functions?

7. Give the broadest definition possible of a document?

8. What is the golden rule regarding detail?

9. What is meant by the term, "continuity of concept"?

10. Why is it important to have a common language, or a language in common?

11. What should be the prime source of instrumentation symbols and identification?

12. When are words important on drawings? How are they used?

REFERENCES

1. ISA-5.1-1984 (R1992), Instrument Symbols and Identification

2. ISA-5.4-1991, Instrument Loop Diagrams

2

THE ELEMENTS OF SYMBOLISM

▨ INTRODUCTION: THE BUILDING BLOCKS

Instrumentation does not exist without a process to measure or control. This statement may sound like a truism, but it bears remembering. Too many become so enthralled with the internal workings of instruments and instrument systems that they neglect the basic fact that what they are trying to do is to make a process operate well or better. The application of instrumentation to measurement and control is what is important, not necessarily the internal working of instruments. The choice of symbols and identifiers becomes easier if we bear this in mind.

Another point to remember is that in the early days of instrumentation devices were few and generally self-contained, for example, the steam engine governor (Figure 2-1) or the pressure relief (or safety) valve (Figure 2-2). Symbolism, if necessary at all, was fairly simple and could follow the outline of the device being represented. As more instrumentation was needed and as processes became remotely controlled, symbols were required for panel-mounted devices (Figure 2-3), for signals (Figure 2-4), for transmitters (Figure 2-5), for valves (Figure 2-6), and so on. So many different instruments where developed that it became necessary to symbolize and identify them by category of device or signal (Figure 2-7). This symbolization by general characteristic is a process of abstraction.

Although the abstraction process resulted in symbols looking less like the devices they represented, the symbols were still closely identified with unique, individual devices. This close association of symbol and device created play/control systems (Figure 2-8). The lack of uniquely identifiable devices in the central system caused much mental anguish among those who were accustomed to tangible control devices.

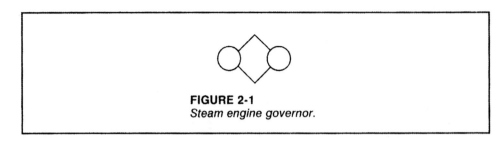

FIGURE 2-1
Steam engine governor.

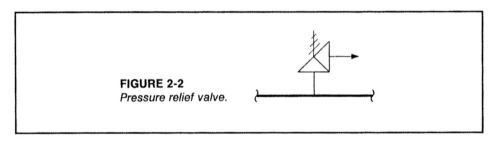

FIGURE 2-2
Pressure relief valve.

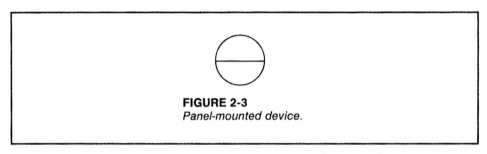

FIGURE 2-3
Panel-mounted device.

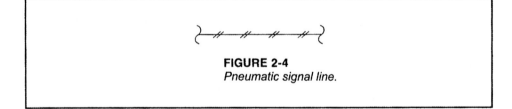

FIGURE 2-4
Pneumatic signal line.

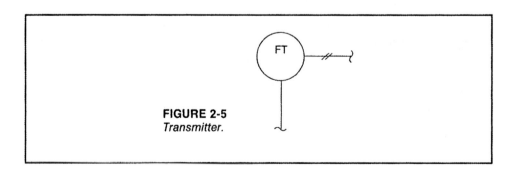

FIGURE 2-5
Transmitter.

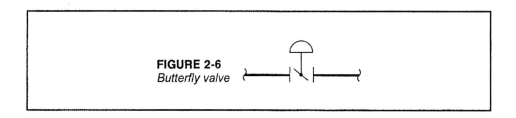

FIGURE 2-6
Butterfly valve

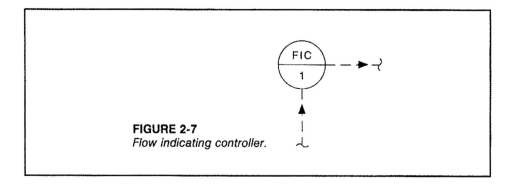

FIGURE 2-7
Flow indicating controller.

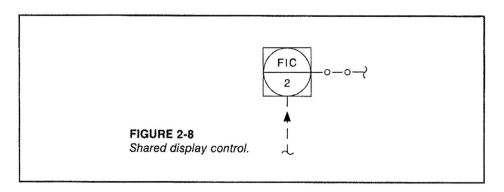

FIGURE 2-8
Shared display control.

Such mental anguish is unnecessary if one keeps in mind how control devices come about. Someone wants a process to be influenced in a certain way or to measure some of its characteristics. Therefore, a device is developed to perform certain functions. What escapes many is the *functions being performed* are what is important, not the "make and model" of the device. The same functions could be performed by many different devices—and are. Unfortunately, the mental connection is often stronger to the device than to the function. Fortunately, the advent of computer-based, shared control systems forced many to make the connection more readily, and the standards are broadening definitions, symbols, and identification to apply to both hardware and function.

Nevertheless, even though the above would suggest that one need think only in terms of function, not hardware, it is necessary to distinguish between the two. Or perhaps it is more accurate to say that it is often necessary to describe the

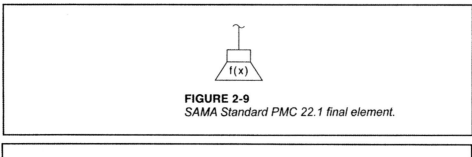

FIGURE 2-9
SAMA Standard PMC 22.1 final element.

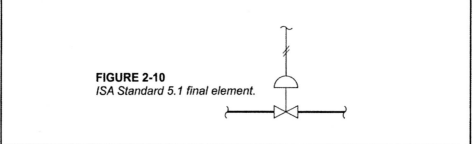

FIGURE 2-10
ISA Standard 5.1 final element.

hardware associated with a function more specifically. The oft used, particularly in the power industry, Scientific Apparatus Makers Association (SAMA) Standard PMC 22.1, *Functional Diagramming of Instrument and Control Systems** is a case in point. It is a very satisfying document intellectually, but some of its concepts, such as the symbol for the final control element in Figure 2-9, have not been broadly accepted, probably since they are a bit too abstract. Most practioners seem to prefer a symbol that is somewhat more physical such as the control valve in Figure 2-10.

Before discussing specific symbols, it is worthwhile to repeat the comparison between language and symbols. It probably is possible to have an entirely rational symbolism and identification system, just as some scholars would like to see an entirely rational (and universal) language—but none exists. The successive members of the Académie Francaise, charged with perfecting the French language since Richelieu in 1635, have never been able to keep up with the communication needs of the French people nor with their penchant for independence. Similarly, in the field of communication of measurement and control concepts, standards committees may give direction, but they cannot dictate. ISA understands this and attempts to ensure that its published standards are based

---

* Prior to when it ceased to exist as a trade group, SAMA relinquished control of this standard to ISA in 1990 for distribution and sale, and for incorporation into standards as appropriate. Function block designations from that standard had already been used with permission to form the basis for Table 3 in the 1984 revision (Reaffirmed 1992) of ISA-5.1.

on consensus. The symbols and identification used in ISA's "5" series of standards have passed the test of consensus. If the reader does not like a specific symbol, before inventing a new one he or she should stop to ask whether or not the symbol is generally accepted as a tool of communication or rethink the device or function to be depicted and perhaps realize that an existing symbol will work. The same applies to identification.

GEOMETRIC FIGURES

Line drawings with geometric shapes are used to represent measurement and control functions, devices, and systems. Certain geometric figures have come to represent certain concepts on specific types of drawings.

General Considerations

First of all, symbol size consistency is important from a presentation viewpoint. Beyond that, symbol and text size may vary according to the user's needs and the type and original size of document being generated, with 3/8" (9-10 mm) diameter being the smallest recommended bubble size. For a typical "D" size (22" x 34") drawing, a bubble of at least 9/16 " (14-15 mm) diameter is recommended, as is a square or diamond of 1/4" x 1/4" (6-7 mm x 6-7 mm).Particular attention should be given to text size as "D"s are reduced to 11" x 17 " for review or 11" x 17"s are reduced to 8 1/2" x 11". A common text size for full size sheets is 1/8" (3-4 mm).

The proper use of line weight is important. Make sure that instrument signal lines and "leaders" from bubbles to line-mounted devices are lighter than process lines. And on the subject of leaders, they should be at a 45-degree angle, and not touch the device, to avoid confusion with process connections.

Circles

The circle (or bubble) is used extensively as a general instrument symbol and as a flag. As an instrument symbol it represents the concept of a device or function (Figure 2-11). As a flag it is used to carry information about another symbol that represents a device or a function (Figure 2-12).

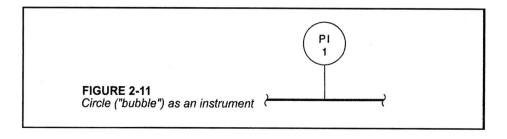

FIGURE 2-11
Circle ("bubble") as an instrument

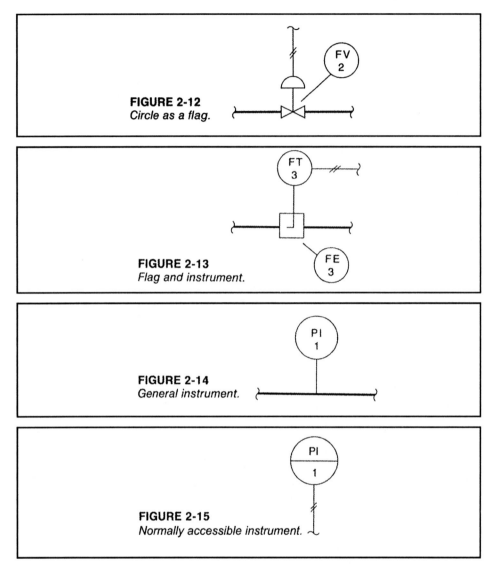

FIGURE 2-12
Circle as a flag.

FIGURE 2-13
Flag and instrument.

FIGURE 2-14
General instrument.

FIGURE 2-15
Normally accessible instrument.

The distinction between the two uses is made by drawing a lead line (or leader) from the circle used as a flag at an angle, so it will not be confused with an impulse line or process line, for example, and by making sure that a visible gap exists between it and the symbol for the instrument (Figure 2-13).

The flag circle is used to carry a tag number. The instrument circle not only may carry a tag number, but it may be modified to convey more detailed information, depending on the document on which the symbol is used. It is important to keep in mind this latter distinction. The simplest symbol, a circle for instance, is used to represent a general instrument on a process flow diagram (Figure 2-14). No attempt is made to infer panel mounting or local mounting. On a more detailed engineering flow diagram, the distinction is made by drawing a solid

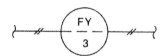

FIGURE 2-16
Not normally accessible instrument.

FIGURE 2-17
Normally accessible auxiliary panel.

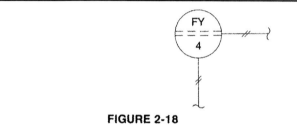

FIGURE 2-18
Not normally accessible auxiliary panel.

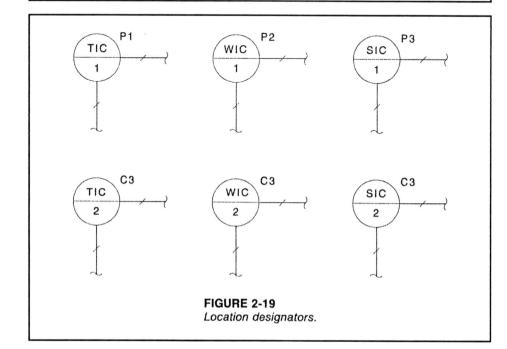

FIGURE 2-19
Location designators.

line across the circle for devices that are mounted on the front of the panel, Visual Display Unit (VDU), console (normally accessible to the operator) (Figure 2-15) and a dashed line for devices that are mounted behind the panel (normally not accessible to the operator) (Figure 2-16). We symbolize an auxiliary panel, i.e., not the main one, by double solid (Figure 2-17) or double dashed lines (Figure 2-18).

When there are several panel locations and when it is difficult to decide which is the main panel or which is an auxiliary panel, letters and numbers located as superscripts may be used to designate one panel form another (P1, P2, P3). Alternatively, if the device is mounted on a console, C1, C2, and C3 may be used (Figure 2-19). For instrument racks, R1, R2, and R3 could be the designators. Whatever system is used, the nomenclature should be clearly denoted in some form of legend.

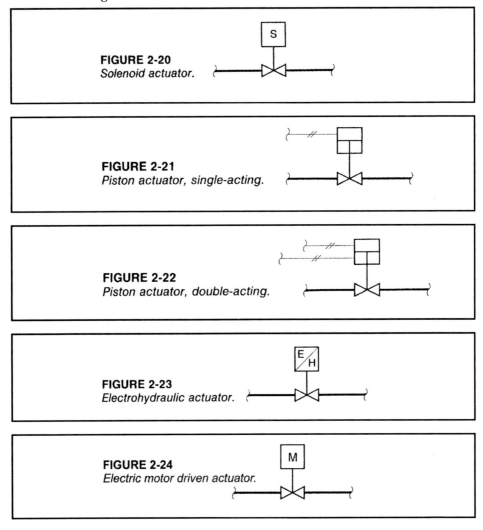

FIGURE 2-20
Solenoid actuator.

FIGURE 2-21
Piston actuator, single-acting.

FIGURE 2-22
Piston actuator, double-acting.

FIGURE 2-23
Electrohydraulic actuator.

FIGURE 2-24
Electric motor driven actuator.

Small Squares

One of the earliest and most common uses for a small square was to represent a solenoid actuator. Some inscribed the square with an S, some did not. ISA prefers to inscribe the square with an S since the letter serves to clearly distinguish this function from many others (Figure 2-20).

The small square also is used for piston actuators, with a T-bar that represents the piston and single or double signal lines to show single-acting (Figure 2-21) or double-acting (Figure 2-22) cylinders. We may represent other actuators by inscribing the small square with E/H for an electro hydraulic actuator (Figure 2-23) or an M for an electric motor driven actuator (Figure 2-24).

The small square may also be used to represent a positioner. It is drawn adjacent to a valve stem (Figure 2-25).

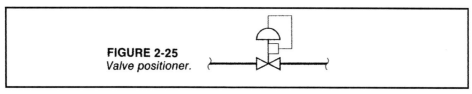

FIGURE 2-25
Valve positioner.

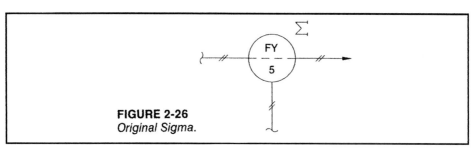

FIGURE 2-26
Original Sigma.

The most recent development is the use of the small square to represent a function block or a function designator. This is very similar to the use of a circle as an instrument or as an instrument flag, and confusion can result if the distinction between the two uses is not kept in mind. Sigma (Σ), the function designator for algebraic addition, for example, was originally used as a "superscript" above and to the right of a relay bubble (circle) to specify what type of device was signified by the letter Y (Figure 2-26). Later, it became common to set off the Sigma in a small box to avoid confusion with other markings on a flow sheet (Figure 2-27). Later still, it became popular to use the box inscribed with the function symbol as a stand-alone symbol, usually on conceptual drawings when tagging was not necessary (Figure 2-28).

Even later, another use emerged with the advent of shared control systems.It became convenient to user the small box contiguous to a larger one, representing

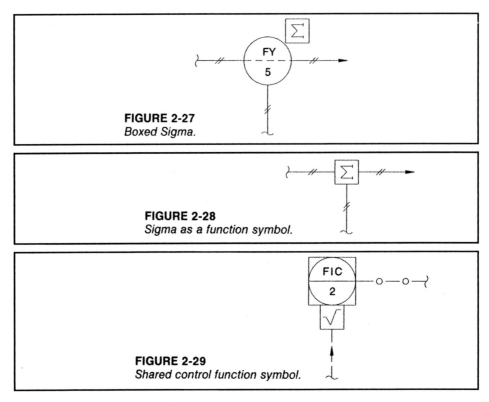

FIGURE 2-27
Boxed Sigma.

FIGURE 2-28
Sigma as a function symbol.

FIGURE 2-29
Shared control function symbol.

the shared control function. This representation allowed for an economy of symbols in depicting complex functions (Figure 2-29).

Small squares are beginning to be used as symbols for inline flowmeters, and, when shown on engineering flow sheets, are often accompanied by bubbles (balloons, circles) used as flags (Figure 2-30). Similarly, they are used to represent traps, although many purists will deny that a trap is an instrument (Figure 2-31).

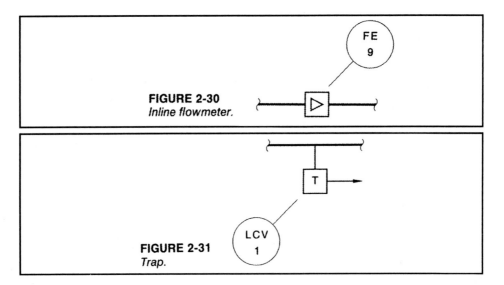

FIGURE 2-30
Inline flowmeter.

FIGURE 2-31
Trap.

Large Squares

Again, the advent of shared control and shared display required a distinction to be drawn between so-called conventional (meaning unique, discrete) instruments and shared control/display functions that performed the same job but could not be so readily recognized as belonging in a unique housing. The solution was to draw a square around the circle that represented the instrument (Figure 2-32). Continuity of concept is involved in leaving the original bubble in place. Many have argued for its abolition, but most feel more comfortable with the circle inscribed in the square. The combination of large squares and small squares leads to some intriguing combinations, and the difference between function blocks and function designators (flags) is made according to whether a signal line strikes the box (Figure 2-33) or whether the box is tangent to a larger square (Figure 2-34).

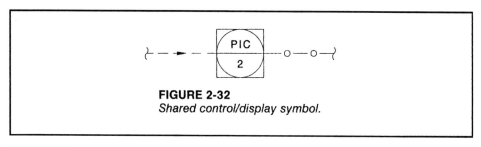

FIGURE 2-32
Shared control/display symbol.

FIGURE 2-33
Function block.

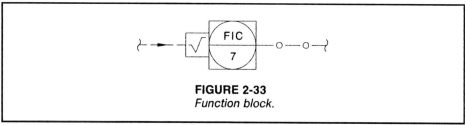

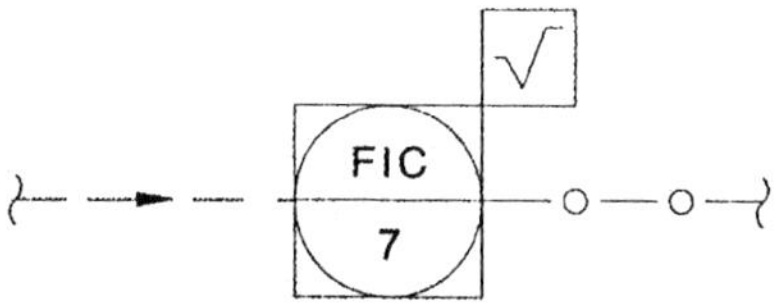

FIGURE 2-34
Function designator.

Triangles and Their Combinations

Combinations of triangles find their greatest use in symbolizing valve bodies. The general symbol for any kind of valve body is the "bow tie" formed by two triangles with their apexes touching (Figure 2-35). The angle valve (Figure 2-36),

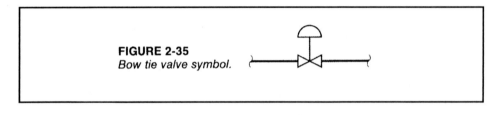

FIGURE 2-35
Bow tie valve symbol.

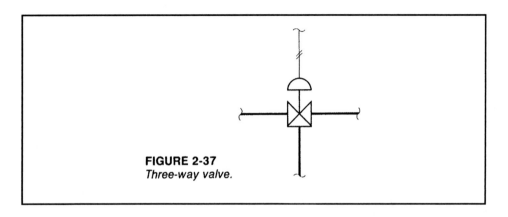

FIGURE 2-36
Angle valve.

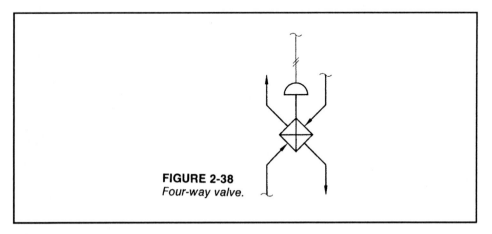

FIGURE 2-37
Three-way valve.

FIGURE 2-38
Four-way valve.

the three-way valve (Figure 2-37), and the four-way valve (Figure 2-38) body symbols are also very popular. The triangle also makes its appearance in an oblong to represent a rupture disk (Figure 2-39) and attached to a circle to represent a variable area flowmeter (rotameter) (Figure 2-40).

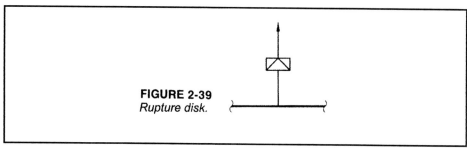

FIGURE 2-39
Rupture disk.

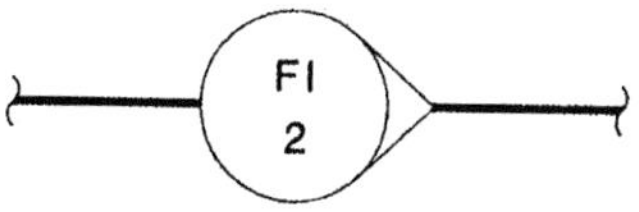

FIGURE 2-40
Variable area flowmeter.

Diamonds

Diamonds are used to represent patchboard connections (Figure 2-41), instrument purges (Figure 2-42), reset functions (Figure 2-43), general interlock symbols (Figure 2-44), and simple logic gates on other than detailed drawings (Figure 2-45 and 2-46).

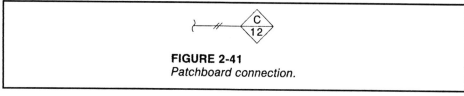

FIGURE 2-41
Patchboard connection.

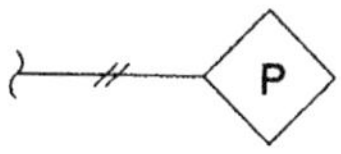

FIGURE 2-42
Purge.

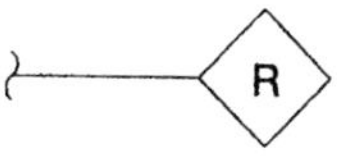

FIGURE 2-43
Reset function.

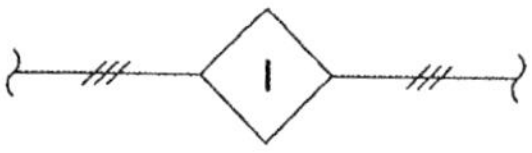

FIGURE 2-44
General interlock.

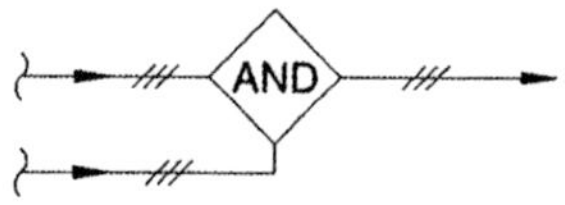

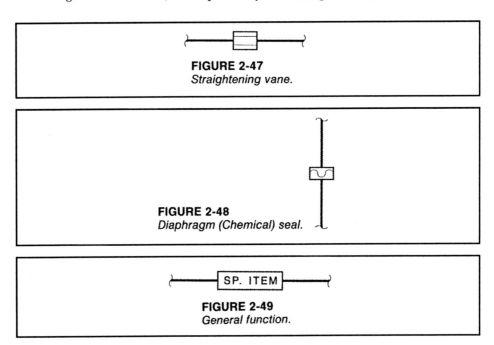

FIGURE 2-45
AND gate on flow diagram.

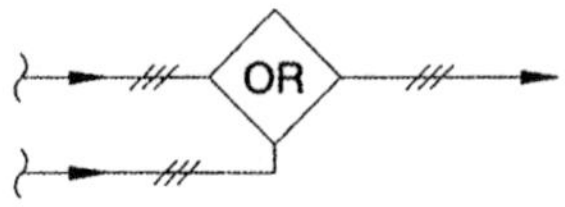

FIGURE 2-46
OR gate on flow diagram.

Oblongs

Oblongs with other lines inside represent straightening vanes (horizontal straight lines) (Figure 2-47), diaphragm (chemical) seals (wavy lines) (Figure 2-48), or some general function (lines replaced by words)(Figure 2-49).

FIGURE 2-47
Straightening vane.

FIGURE 2-48
Diaphragm (Chemical) seal.

SP. ITEM

FIGURE 2-49
General function.

Half Circles or Curves

The most common use of the half circle is probably to represent a diaphragm operator (Figure 2-50). Two curves in juxtaposition represent a double-acting diaphragm operator (Figure 2-51). The half circle symbol has become so popular that it is often used to represent a general actuator, whether or not it is a diaphragm actuator.

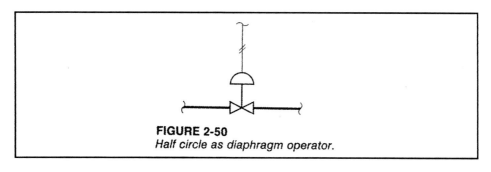

FIGURE 2-50
Half circle as diaphragm operator.

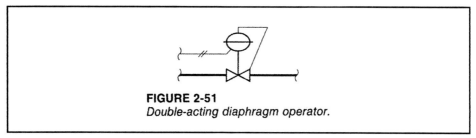

FIGURE 2-51
Double-acting diaphragm operator.

▓ LINES

Lines are used to represent signals. It is important to distinguish between signals, i.e., information and wires. Wires become important only when it is necessary to know how to connect them. Until that time the signal is usually more important. Typical line weights are aaa x bbb.

If a drawing is simple and concerns instrumentation concepts to a greater extent than it does process concepts (in other words, if there are few process lines and more instrument lines), a simple line serves to represent the flow of signal information from one device or function to another. However, when instrumentation symbolism is part of a drawing that is not exclusively an instrument drawing or that is very complex, it often becomes necessary to differentiate among types of signals. It is also often necessary to have a symbol for an undifferentiated signal line when the designer knows what he or she wants to do but has not yet decided how specifically to do it.

The principle signal lines are:
1. the undefined signal symbol drawn as a solid line with single crosshatches (Figure 2-52);
2. the pneumatic signal symbol drawn with double crosshatches (Figure 2-53);
3. the electrical signal symbol drawn as a dashed line (Figure 2-54);
4. the alternative electrical (electronic) signal symbol drawn with triple crosshatches (Figure 2-55);

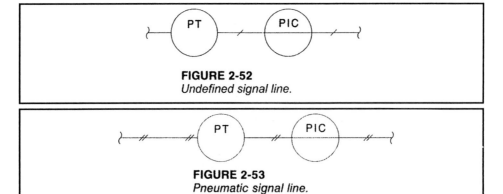

FIGURE 2-52
Undefined signal line.

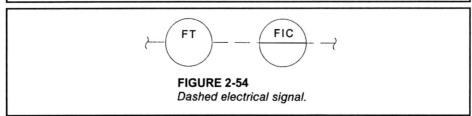

FIGURE 2-53
Pneumatic signal line.

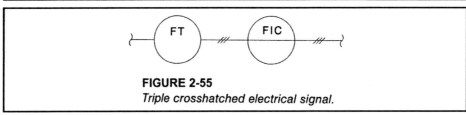

FIGURE 2-54
Dashed electrical signal.

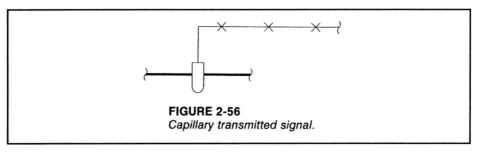

FIGURE 2-55
Triple crosshatched electrical signal.

5. the capillary tubing (filled system) signal drawn as a solid line with small crosses (Figure 2-56);
6. the hydraulic signal symbol drawn as a solid line with right angles (L's) across it (Figure 2-57);
7. the guided electromagnetic or sonic signal line drawn as a solid line with sinusoids (Figure 2-58);

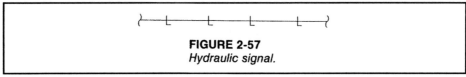

FIGURE 2-56
Capillary transmitted signal.

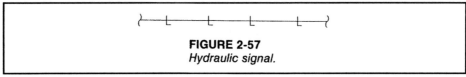

FIGURE 2-57
Hydraulic signal.

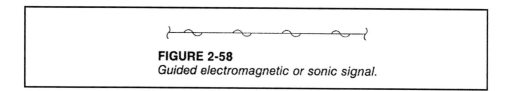

FIGURE 2-58
Guided electromagnetic or sonic signal.

8. the unguided electromagnetic or sonic signal drawn as a series of sinusoids (Figure 2-59);

9. the internal system, or software, link drawn as a series of dashes and small open circles (Figure 2-60); and

10. the mechanical link drawn as a disjointed line with small solid circles (Figure 2-61).

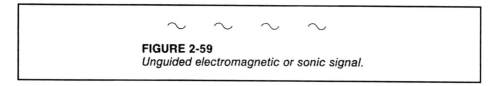

FIGURE 2-59
Unguided electromagnetic or sonic signal.

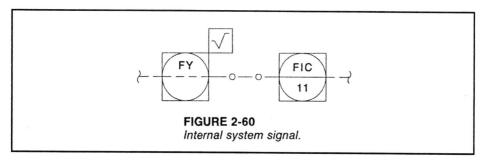

FIGURE 2-60
Internal system signal.

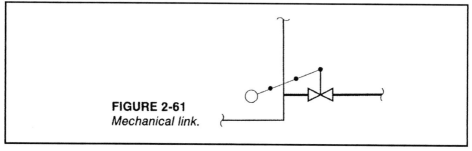

FIGURE 2-61
Mechanical link.

The above line symbols are used primarily for analog signals, but frequently no distinction is made between analog and on-off (binary) signals. In most cases this makes no difference since the signal type may be inferred from the context. A momentary push button is a binary device, which, when connected to another device by an electrical signal line symbol, is clearly understood to be an on-off device even though the electrical signal line symbol is usually associated with analog signals (Figure 2-62).

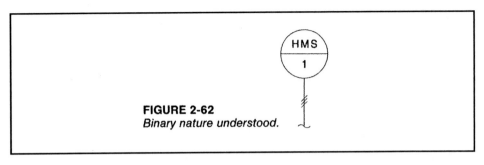

FIGURE 2-62
Binary nature understood.

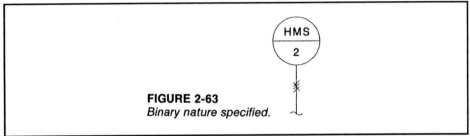

FIGURE 2-63
Binary nature specified.

However, it sometimes becomes necessary or desirable to differentiate between the two types of signals, especially in the batch processing chemical industries. When it is important to distinguish between them, the reverse slash is used across the crosshatches of the basic line symbols for electric binary signals (Figure 2-63). Again, there is nothing like a legend to tell the reader of a document what the designer intends, just in case the reader is not familiar with a certain convention.

▓ SUMMARY

The application of instrumentation to measurement and control should be the focal point of the symbolic representation of measurement and control systems. The technology involved is secondary.

The use of symbols is a process of abstraction in which the salient characteristics of a device or a function are portrayed by some simple geometric construction. This abstraction process has been difficult for many to grasp, since functions, until recently, usually have been associated with specific devices. Computer-based control systems force easier acceptance of the use of symbols for functions that are not readily identified with a unique piece of hardware. There is, however, often a need to think in terms of hardware and to describe this hardware more specifically.

In choosing symbols to depict ideas, it is wise to remember that the person who receives the communication must understand the symbols and should not be confused or irritated by them; otherwise, the transfer of information is hindered.

The standards of ISA—The Instrumentation, Systems, and Automation Society, are a widely accepted source of symbols. ISA's "5" series of standards have met the test of consensus, i.e., they have met with substantial agreement from a large body of standards users and they have stood the test of time.

Line drawings with simple geometric shapes represent functions, devices, and systems. Geometric shapes depict certain concepts on specific documents. Circles can be used to depict an instrument (or function) or as a flag. Small squares are used to symbolize functions (or instruments) and as function designators (a form of flag). Lines are used to represent signal flow. Some degree of flexibility in the level of detail may be chosen to depict concepts; therefore, it is a good idea to use a legend to define the intentions of the designer.

QUESTIONS

1. Where should the focus be when choosing symbols and identifiers? On the instruments or on the process? Why?

2. Historically, how has the intellectual abstraction process of describing devices and function by symbols been broadened?

3. What is the basis (and strength) of a consensus standard such as ISA-5.1-1984 (R1992)?

4. Geometric figures serve as the basis for representing both devices and functions. Some figures have subtle differences to represent different concepts

5. Why are legend sheets so important?

REFERENCES

1. ISA-5.1-1984 (R1992), Instrumentation Symbols and Identification

2. ISA-5.2-1976 (R1992), Binary Logic Diagrams for Process Operations.

3. ISA-5.2-1983, Graphic Symbols for Distributed Control/Shared Display Instrumentation, Logic, and Computer Systems

4. ISA-5.4-1991, Instrument Loop Diagrams.

5. ISA-5.5-1985, Graphic Symbols for Process Displays.

THE ELEMENTS OF IDENTIFICATION

▓ INTRODUCTION: BUILDING BLOCK NAMES

This chapter introduces the elements that constitute the basis for some very necessary bookkeeping. Control systems engineers and designers who work in a production engineering environment soon learn the importance of having an identification system that simply and uniquely identifies each of the thousands of instruments and functions with which they must deal (Ref.1). Operating and maintenance personnel instinctively understand the importance of being able to identify and keep track of every element that contributes to the well-being of their plant. Bookkeeping usually is thought of as a very dry subject, which is studied only grudgingly and out of painful necessity. Instrument identification sometimes is treated similarly, to the ultimate regret of those who do so.

Although this chapter discusses identification separately from symbols, the reader should bear in mind the close connection between the two under most circumstances.

On drawings, symbols and identification go hand in hand. The functional part of the identifier (FIC, for instance) helps qualify the general symbol as belonging to the category "Flow-Indicating Controller"; the numerical part (101, for example) identifies the flow indicting control device or function specifically. Symbols and identifiers or, at least, symbols and the functional identification portion of the identifier are really inseparable as far as drawings are concerned. For instrument indexes and data sheets, identifying tag numbers stand alone without supporting symbols.

▓ BASIC IDENTIFICATION (TAG NUMBERS)

What is meant by "tag number" (Figure 3-1)? Obviously, the tag number is the number on the metal, plastic, or paper "tag" that is wired, screwed, or stuck to an instrument. But there are alpha characters as well as numeric on the tag. Do these form part of the tag number? And what about "functions" in a shared control or a computer control system in which there is no discrete instrument upon which to hang a "tag"? Should these disembodied instruments be "tagged"?

Evidently, the designation "tag number" is a traditional one that has been carried over from a less complex time. In ISA terminology, it is the alphanumeric code that uniquely identifies an instrument or function. Note that functions not associated with discrete instruments may have to be tagged because engineers and designers may have to "configure" them. To put it simply, anything worthy of being talked about may be worthy of being tagged, even if one cannot associate a specific, discrete instrument with it.

An alphanumeric identification system may not seem too important in a small facility with very few instruments. After all, an instrument may be named for its function: kettle temperature controller, for instance. However, medium to large complexes may have thousands to tens of thousands of unique devices or functions that must be kept track of if they are to be procured, installed, and maintained correctly. It does not take many instruments to make an identification scheme very important.

Several schemes are in use at present; ISA's is based on utility, simplicity, and universality and has stood the test of time. Some systems tend to rely heavily on mnemonics (American Petroleum Institute's API RP 14C, for instance). They are not universal. They are useful in a very narrow area of application but lose their usefulness when they are applied to larger fields. Although many of these schemes claim to be based on ISA methods, they are like dialects in a language—they are difficult for the uninitiated to understand. The ISA method, originally documented by ISA-RP-5.1 as first issued in 1949, is more rational. It has been developed by concensus and by use over the years, has stood the test of time, and is recognized as a good communication tool.

The ISA identification method uses an alphanumeric designation code. The alpha portion consists of uppercase letters, preferably not more than four;

the numeric part consists of numbers as low as one and preferably not more than 9999. Smaller numbers are easier to remember and fit better into instrument bubbles on drawings. The entire alphanumeric code is called a tag number. Two examples may be seen in Figure 3-1.

Typical Tag Number

TIC 103   –   Instrument Identification or Tag Number
TIC   –   Functional Identification
T   103 –   Loop Identification
     103 –   Loop Number
T   –   First Letter
  IC   –   Succeeding Letters

Expanded Tag Number

10-PAH-5A –   Tag Number
10   –   Optional Prefix (plant or area number)
       A   –   Optional Suffix

Note: Hyphens are optional as separators.

FIGURE 3-1
Tag numbers.

FUNCTIONAL IDENTIFICATION

The alpha portion of the tag number is the functional identification. It precedes the numeric part (the loop number). In fact, on conceptual drawings and initial engineering drawings, the functional identification is often used alone since, when taken with an instrument bubble, it supplies all the information necessary for understanding the basic function (Figure 3-2). The numeric part may be added later if and when it becomes necessary to specifically identify a device or function (Figure 3-3).

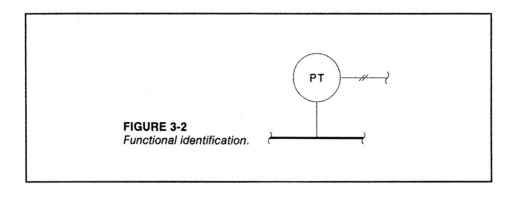

FIGURE 3-2
Functional identification.

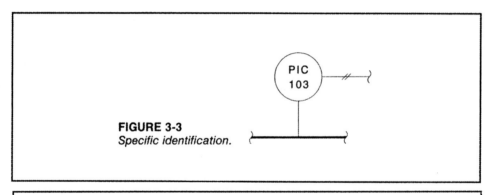

FIGURE 3-3
Specific identification.

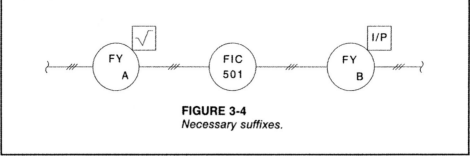

FIGURE 3-4
Necessary suffixes.

Figure 3-1 shows that the tag number may be dissected into its various component parts. The entire code is called the tag number or instrument identification. The functional identification is a shorthand description of what the device or function does. The first letter taken with the numeric portion is the loop identification. The loop identification is used to identify the loop as a whole without reference to its component parts and is often used as the reference base in instrument indexes. The loop number is the numeric portion of the tag number. The distinction between loop identification and loop number is that the former supplies information about the measured or initiating variable, while the latter does not. In addition, there are two variants of the ISA tag numbering system: serial and parallel numbering. The parallel numbering system requires the first letter for complete loop identification; the serial method does not. The two variants will be discussed in more detail later in this chapter. The terms "first letter" and "succeeding letters" are self-evident. They simply permit discussion of the component parts of the functional identification.

In refinery practice, and elsewhere where there are many plant units or areas, it is often necessary to add a prefix to designate the area or unit. The use of a prefix, instead of incorporating the area or unit number into the body of the tag number, allows greater flexibility and maintains the simplicity of the basic system. The prefix may be omitted from drawings that refer only to one unit or area. A single note on the drawing suffices, and the tags fit the bubbles better.

An optional suffix becomes a necessary suffix if one wishes to distinguish among several devices, each with a similar functional identification. A square root extractor and a current-to-pressure converter in the same loop are examples (Figure 3-4).

The ISA identification method breaks up the alpha functional identification into a first letter with a modifying letter, if necessary, and a succeeding letter or succeeding letters, also with a modifier, if necessary. The first letter designates a measured or initiating variable; succeeding letters designate readout, passive, or output functions (Table 3-1). For example, the letters TA designate a temperature alarm; the first letter T represents temperature; the succeeding letter A represents alarm. T is a measured variable; A is an output function. In TDAH two modifiers are added: D, differential, modifies T and the letters constitute a

TABLE 3-1
Identification Letters

| First Letter | | Succeeding Letters | | |
Measured or Initiating Variable	Modifier	Readout or Passive Function	Output Function	Modifier
A Analysis		Alarm		
B Burner, Combustion		User's Choice	User's Choice	User's Choice
C User's Choice			Control	
D User's Choice	Differential			
E Voltage		Sensor (Primary Element)		
F Flow Rate	Ratio (Fraction)			
G User's Choice		Glass, Viewing Device		
H Hand				High
I Current (Electrical)		Indicate		
J Power	Scan			
K Time, Time Schedule	Time, Rate of Change		Control Station	
L Level		Light		Low
M User's Choice	Momentary			Middle, Intermediate
N User's Choice		User's Choice	User's Choice	User's Choice
O User's Choice		Orifice, Restriction		
P Pressure, Vacuum		Point, (Test) Connection		
Q Quantity	Integrate, Totalize			
R Radiation		Record		
S Speed, Frequency	Safety		Switch	
T Temperature			Transmit	
U Multivariable		Multifunction	Multifunction	Multifunction
V Vibration, Mechanical Analysis			Valve, Damper, Louver	
W Weight, Force		Well		
X Unclassified	X Axis	Unclassified	Unclassified	Unclassified
Y Event, State, or Presence	Y Axis		Relay, Compute, Convert	
Z Position, Dimension	Z Axis		Driver, Actuator, Unclassified Final Control Element	

new measured variable; H, high, modifies A. Note that temperature and temperature differential are different process variables.

Table 3-1 shows that all twenty-six letters of the alphabet are used as first letters. Some letters take on different meanings as succeeding letters and as modifiers.

Four general categories of letters are:
1. designated letters such as E (voltage) or T (temperature);
2. user's choice letters such as M, as a measured or as an initiating variable, or such as N for all uses;
3. the unclassified letter, X; and
4. the multivariable or multifunction letter, U.

The designated letters are reasonably specific: T (temperature), F (flow), L (level). Exceptions to this specificity are A (analysis) and V (vibration, mechanical analysis). The letter A has always been a catchall for all types of analyses, both chemical and physical, and its use requires a subscript or superscript outside the bubble (Figure 3-5) for greater specificity. The letter V was originally used for the variable viscosity, but, since viscosity measurement is a form of analytical measurement, viscosity was moved into the A category, freeing V for other uses. Vibration was an obvious choice, and as machinery monitoring or mechanical analysis was becoming more and more import, the 5.1 Standards Committee successfully proposed its use for mechanical analysis in a role similar to that of A in more general analyses. The use of V for vibration combined with the modifiers X, Y, and Z to represent the major axes of a machine can convey very specific information (Figure 3-6).

User's choice letters generally are those for which no clear consensus has developed in terms of usage. They may be applied for different purposes in different industries, and they are best specifically defined on a legend sheet. The letter C, for instance, may be used for "conductivity" in the chemical industry and for the measured variable "consistency" in the pulp and paper industry, although the phonetic "K" is also used in pulp and paper for "consistency."

The meaning of the unclassified letter X has been somewhat distorted in the past. It was intended that X be used for those one-of-a-kind, unlisted meanings that might occur infrequently. In fact, X suffered from overwork as a catchall, especially in the area of on-off logic. The adoption of Y for event, state, or presence variables and of V for mechanical analysis should alleviate this situation. Suffice it to say that X should be defined where it is used, and it

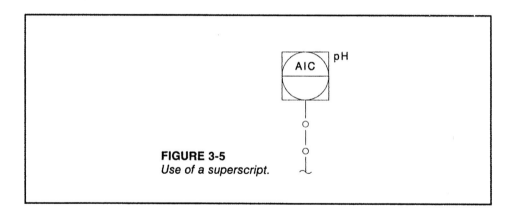

FIGURE 3-5
Use of a superscript.

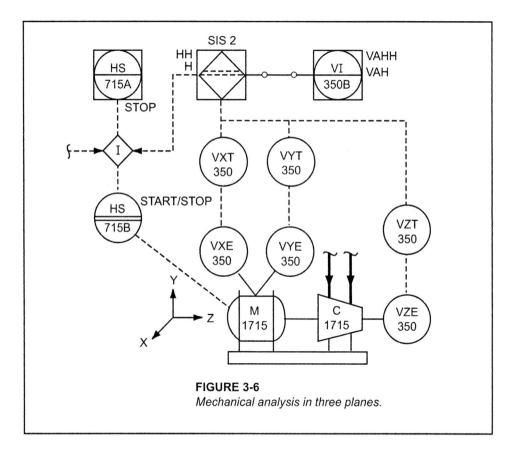

FIGURE 3-6
Mechanical analysis in three planes.

should be used sparingly, not as another user's choice variable.

The event, state, or presence variable Y is intended to be used where control or monitoring responses are event-driven (as is the case with many programmable logic controllers) as distinct from time- or time schedule-driven responses, which use the initiating variable K. Y is also used when the presence or absence of something is being sensed or when a binary state is being ascertained.

▧ LEGITIMATE FUNCTION DESIGNATORS

In an attempt to facilitate the choice of "legitimate" function designators, ISA-5.1 reintroduced a table called *"Typical Letter Combinations,"* reproduced here as

TABLE 3-2 (A)
Typical Letter Combinations

| | | Controllers | | | Self-Actuated Control Valves |
First-Letters	Initiating or Measured Variable	Recording	Indicating	Blind	
A	Analysis	ARC	AIC	AC	
B	Burner/ Combustion	BRC	BIC	BC	
C	User's Choice				
D	User's Choice				
E	Voltage	ERC	EIC	EC	
F	Flow Rate	FRC	FIC	FC	FCV, FICV
FQ	Flow Quantity	FQRC	FQIC		
FF	Flow Ratio	FFRC	FFIC	FFC	
G	User's Choice				
H	Hand		HIC	HC	
I	Current	IRC	IIC		
J	Power	JRC	JIC		
K	Time	KRC	KIC	KC	KCV
L	Level	LRC	LIC	LC	LCV
M	User's Choice				
N	User's Choice				
O	User's Choice				
P	Pressure/Vacuum	PRC	PIC	PC	PCV
PD	Pressure Differential	PDRC	PDIC	PDC	PDCV
Q	Quantity	QRC	QIC		
R	Radiation	RRC	RIC	RC	
S	Speed/Frequency	SRC	SIC	SC	SCV
T	Temperature	TRC	TIC	TC	TCV
TD	Temperature Differential	TDRC	TDIC	TDC	TDCV
U	Multivariable				
V	Vibration, Machinery Analysis				
W	Weight/Force	WRC	WIC	WC	WCV
WD	Weight/Force Differential	WDRC	WDIC	WDC	WDCV
X	Unclassified				
Y	Event, State, Presence			YC	
Z	Position, Dimension	ZRC	ZIC	ZC	ZCV
ZD	Gauging, Deviation	ZDRC	ZDIC	ZDC	ZDCV

...mbinations

First Letters	Readout Devices		Switches and Alarm Devices			Transmitters		
	Recording	Indicating	High	Low	Comb	Recording	Indicating	Blind
A	AR	AI	ASH	ASL	ASHL	ART	AIT	AT
B	BR	BI	BSH	BSL	BSHL	BRT	BIT	BT
C								
D								
E	ER	EI	ESH	ESL	ESHL	ERT	EIT	ET
F	FR	FI	FSH	FSL	FSHL	FRT	FIT	FT
FQ	FQR	FQI	FQSH	FQSL			FQIT	FQT
FF	FFR	FFI	FFSH	FFSL				
G								
H								
I	IR	II	ISH	ISL	ISHL	IRT	IIT	IT
J	JR	JI	JSH	JSL	JSHL	JRT	JIT	JT
K	KR	KI	KSH	KSL	KSHL	KRT	KIT	KT
L	LR	LI	LSH	LSL	LSHL	LRT	LIT	LT
M								
N								
O								
P	PR	PI	PSH	PSL	PSHL	PRT	PIT	PT
PD	PDR	PDI	PDSH	PDSL		PDRT	PDIT	PDT
Q	QR	QI	QSH	QSL	QSHL	QRT	QIT	QT
R	RR	RI	RSH	RSL	RSHL	RRT	RIT	RT
S	SR	SI	SSH	SSL	SSHL	SRT	SIT	ST
T	TR	TI	TSH	TSL	TSHL	TRT	TIT	TT
TD	TDR	TDI	TDSH	TDSL		TDRT	TDIT	TDT
U	UR	UI						
V	VR	VI	VSH	VSL	VSHL	VRT	VIT	VT
W	WR	WI	WSH	WSL	WSHL	WRT	WIT	WT
WD	WDR	WDI	WDSH	WDSL		WDRT	WDIT	WDT
X								
Y	YR	YI	YSH	YSL				YT
Z	ZR	ZI	ZSH	ZSL	ZSHL	ZRT	ZIT	ZT
ZD	ZDR	ZDI	ZDSH	ZDSL		ZDRT	ZDIT	ZDT

Table 3-2. Apart from facilitating the task of choosing common letter combinations, the table was intended to reduce the number of poorly conceived usages that were creeping into industrial practice.

▨ PARALLEL AND SERIAL LOOP NUMBERING

The purpose of the loop number is to identify each loop specifically. The first loop to be numbered could be called loop number one; the second, number two, and so on. This effectively, is what the serial numbering scheme allows. There is no need for anything other than numbers to designate a loop.

TABLE 3-2 (C)
Typical Letter Combinations

First-Letters	Solenoids, Relays, Computing Devices	Primary Element	Test Point	Well or Probe	Viewing Device, Glass	Safety Device	Final Element
A	AY	AE	AP	AW			AV
B	BY	BE		BW	BG		BZ
C							
D							
E	EY	EE					EZ
F	FY	FE	FP		FG		FV
FQ	FQY						FQV
FF		FE					FV
G							
H							
I	IY	IE					IZ
J	JY	JE					JV
K	KY	KE					KV
L	LY	LE		LW	LG		LV
M							
N							
O							
P	PY	PE	PP			PSV, PSE	PV
PD	PDY	PDE	PDP				PDV
Q	QY	QE					QZ
R	RY	RE		RW			RZ
S	SY	SE					SV
T	TY	TE	TP	TW		TSE	TV
TD	TDY	TE	TP	TW			TDV
U	UY						UV
V	VY	VE					VZ
W	WY	WE					WZ
WD	WDY	WE					WDZ
							YZ
Y	YY	YE					YZ
Z	ZY	ZE					ZV
ZD	ZDY	ZDE					ZDV

In very large industrial complexes, the individual numbers can reach five figures with the above serial numbering system. Many do not feel comfortable with such large numbers, nor with the fact that there is no mnemonic to suggest the measured or initiating variables with which the loop is dealing. The parallel numbering system solves both the above problems by allowing a new numeric sequence for each new first letter.

Additional methods can be used to reduce the maximum size of the loop number. For instance, when the expanded tag number is used with the unit or

NOTES TO TABLE 3-2 (A), (B), (C)
Typical Letter Combinations

Note: This table is not all inclusive.

*A, alarm, the annunciating device, may be used in the same fashion as S, switch, the actuating device.

**The letters H and L may be omitted in the undefined case.

Other Possible Combinations:

FO	(Restriction Orifice)
FRK, HIK	(Control Stations
FX	(Accessories)
TJR	(Scanning Recorder)
LLH	(Pilot Light)
FFR	(Ratio)
KQI	(Running Time Indicator)
QQI	(Indicating Counter)
WKIC	(Rate-of-Weight-Loss Controller)
HMS	(Hand Momentary Switch)

area prefix, the unit or area may be treated as a new plant, and the numbering sequence may be started afresh.

CODING

It is tempting to use the loop number for coding purposes, and it is possible to set aside blocks of numbers to differentiate pressure gages from pressure receiving indictors, for example. Many would like to differentiate safety devices from process control devices, but the problem is that one person's safety may be another's operating control.

Experience shows that the best tag numbering system is the simplest one. Although it may seem a good idea at the time to invent a coding system, not every possibility can be foreseen, and the newly made rules end up being broken sooner or later. Confusion results. If you must code the loop number, use the method setting aside blocks of numbers. Do not change the basic system.

SUMMARY

Symbols and identifying tag numbers (at least the alpha portion) go hand in hand on drawings, but on data sheets and other documents identifiers may stand alone.

The tag number is the alphanumeric code that uniquely identifies an instrument or function. Since in large industrial complexes tens of thousands of devices or functions may require identification, it is important to use an identification system that is simple and universal for installation, checkout, maintenance, and other purposes. ISA-5.1 provides such a system.

The alpha portion of the tag number supplies the functional identification, while the numeric part, plus any suffix, adds uniqueness to the tag number.

Two numbering systems exist within ISA-5.1: the parallel and the serial. Both are fundamentally similar. The main difference is that in the parallel numbering system a new numeric sequence is started with each new measured or initiating variable.

Many wish to code the tag numbers. Experience shows that the best system is the simplest. If you must code, use blocks of numbers; do not invent a new numbering system.

▧ QUESTIONS

1. Why, in the introduction, was the parallel drawn between an instrument identification system and 'very necessary' bookkeeping?
2. Is there a difference between: tag number and identification number? Tag number and loop number?
3. Why are some of the non-ISA methods of symbols and identification described as dialects in a language?
4. What is the strength of the ISA system?
5. What part of the tag number is called the functional identification?
6. When and where is the functional identification used alone?
7. What is the difference between serial and parallel numbering systems?
8. Can you tell the difference between serial and parallel systems, at first glance, if the method being used is not specifically defined on a legend sheet?
9. Of what utility is a loop prefix?
10. Is it clear in your mind that a modified first letter represents a different measured or initiating variable?

11. Define clearly the differences among: designated letters; user's choice letters; unclassified letters; multivariable; and multifunction letters.

12. Why was the use of the letter V for machinery monitoring or mechanical analysis compared to the use of the letter A for chemical or physical analysis?

13. What does the term 'consistency' mean and why is the letter C a user's choice letter?

14. Why was the letter X described as a catchall letter and what did the ISA committee do about it?

15. What is the fundamental difference between the letters Y and K?

16. Why did the ISA committee re-introduce the table entitled Typical Letter Combinations?

17. What are the authors' recommendations on the use of numbers for coding purposes?

REFERENCES

1. ISA-5.1-1984 (R1992), Instrumentation Symbols and Identification

2. API RP 14C, American Petroleum Institute Recommended Practice for Analysis, Design, Installation and testing of Basic Surface Safety Systems for Offshore Production Platforms, Seventh Edition, March, 2001.

4

PROCESS FLOW DIAGRAMS

▦ INTRODUCTION: KNOW THE PROCESS

Two major types of flow diagrams are of primary importance to control systems professionals: process flow diagrams and engineering flow diagrams. Process flow diagrams are more standardized throughout the industry than are engineering flow diagrams. Process flow diagrams are generally designated as PFDs. Engineering flow diagrams (EFDs) are also called mechanical flow diagrams (MFDs) and piping (or process) and instrument diagrams (P&IDs). PFDs are typically developed by a process engineering group and P&IDs by the mechanical/piping group. Control systems engineers should be closely involved in both types of drawings at an early stage.

These drawings are most often developed by engineering constructors for their clients, the operating companies. The operating companies also develop them to a lesser extent. Although the drawings carry similar names throughout the industry, they differ in style and content from one company to another.

Control systems engineers are primarily concerned with process flow diagrams and engineering flow diagrams. They are concerned with the PFDs in order to understand the process and obtain the basic information necessary to do their conceptual engineering and with the EFDs in order to record the final design in detail.

Some companies formally develop another type of flow diagram that depicts the control systems in detail but reduces the clutter that is normally associated with the engineering flow diagram. If this control systems flow diagram is not developed formally, it usually is developed informally, since at least a sketch of this nature is necessary to a clear understanding of the control systems.

This chapter is concerned with the process flow diagram from a control systems point of view and will discuss the purpose of the PFD, its utility to control systems personnel, its development, its content, and style. The engineering flow diagram and diagrams used for control systems development will be discussed in subsequent chapters. Although it is not the intent to stray too far from the control systems aspects of the drawings, commonly used process symbols will be offered since they form an integral part of everyday control systems work.

▨ PURPOSE OF THE PROCESS FLOW DIAGRAM

The purpose of the process flow diagram is to depict the fundamental process design, including process flow, process data, unit operations, major equipment, and major piping. It is primarily a working tool of the process engineer during the late conceptualizing stage of the process design and must be completed before any detailed engineering may be begun.

The process flow diagram is usually the earliest major engineering drawing that is developed on a project. It is used to keep all engineering disciplines informed and actively involved in the developing design. It is also used to help ensure process feasibility, continuity, and integrity. It serves to help develop pressure and temperature profile drawings, which establish material selection and pressure/temperature ratings, and in the preparation of equipment specification documents. It is the springboard to the development of the detailed engineering flow diagram.

The purpose of placing instrumentation on a process flow diagram is to document the major controlled and manipulated variables that impact process design. All instruments are not, and should not be, shown on a process flow diagram. A typical process flow diagram is shown in Figure 4-1.

▨ UTILITY TO CONTROL SYSTEMS ENGINEERS

The process flow diagram is the first document that permits a clear understanding of the process to be controlled. It shows the essential elements of the process and gives the operating or design conditions. These, together with the associated material balance, permit a single document to give the control systems engineer a good grasp of the process.

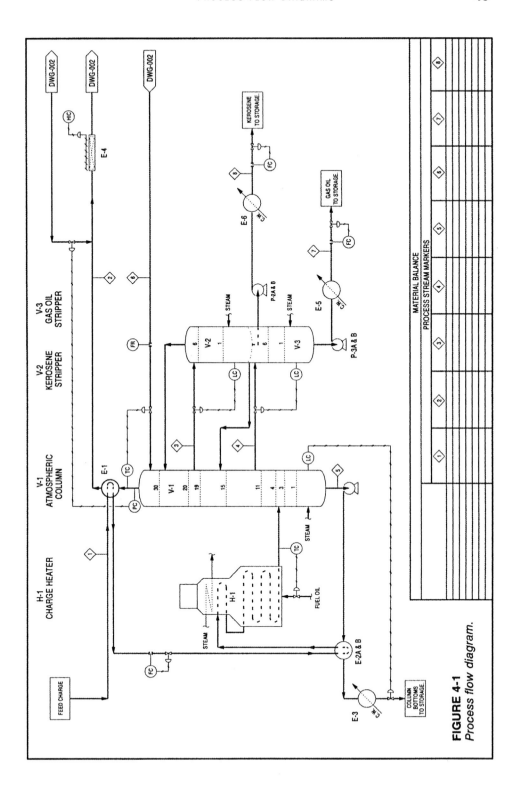

FIGURE 4-1
Process flow diagram.

During initial control systems work, the process flow diagram permits conceptualization of process control strategies. Later, the material balances and operating conditions may be used as input data for the sizing of inline instrumentation and for the selection of instruments.

The very simplicity of the document allows the control systems engineer to work quickly and logically without being faced with the clutter that is usually associated with more detailed engineering drawings. In spite of this simplicity, the process flow diagram carries an enormous amount of information about the process.

To control a process, one must understand it. A process whose inherent characteristics and responses to disturbances are not known cannot be controlled. The process flow diagram is a key element in the control systems engineer's understanding of a given process.

DEVELOPMENT OF THE PFD

The PFD is developed by the process engineer to the point that input from other disciplines is needed. Major control loops are shown in simplified form. The process engineer, who uses past experience with similar process operations, normally draws them. The control systems engineer then analyzes the control problem, makes changes to the diagram, if necessary, and then the two engineers arrive at a mutually satisfactory design approach.

It is extremely important that the control systems engineer not lose this opportunity to influence the design process. Once the process flow diagram has been approved, the entire process, including the control approach taken on the diagram, tends to become "cast in concrete." It then is exceedingly difficult to effect change, even a change for the better.

CONTENT OF THE PFD

The process flow diagram usually contains a single unit operation. Figure 4-1 is a good example. Ideally, a single drawing depicts related equipment and interconnecting piping, which can be isolated conceptually. In other words, a boundary line can be drawn around the related equipment, and the process flows that cross the boundary can be treated as having little influence on upstream or downstream equipment. This is true only within limits, but it helps render the tasks of analysis and design less difficult.

All the major equipment that brings about change within the process is shown on the PFD. All the major process lines are shown. The impact of utility flows (i.e., steam, cooling water) is depicted symbolically and is quantified only by heat duties. Lines are numbered within diamonds, and the diamonds are repeated on the associated material balance. Thus, it is easy to tabulate the material flows and the conditions of each flowing stream. Lines are not sized.

It must be remembered that the PFD is a document created by process engineers in order not only to design a process, but to initiate detailed design by themselves and others. Specific design data associated with the equipment that is finally chosen, therefore, is not available.

Equipment is identified by name and number across the top of the diagram. Heating and cooling duties usually are given under the identification. Minor equipment such as pumps and heat exchangers usually carry the same identification and duty information in proximity to the symbol. Lines carry only operating temperature and pressure information.

It is important to read the notes and any associated legend very carefully. Depending on the information available for particular processes, or depending on a particular company's policy, the conditions given may be design conditions or operating conditions. The information extracted will have to be treated accordingly.

STYLE OF THE PFD

Style relates more to art than to science. However, poor style interferes with information transfer and clear thinking. Good style helps both. Concern for simplicity is often mentioned in this book, but good style is more than mere simplicity. It is a question of the choice of symbols and identifiers and their arrangement, which may appear simple but will convey a maximum of information and understanding. Perhaps style is, after all, also a science. The process flow diagram, when well executed, is the epitome of engineering style.

INSTRUMENTATION SHOWN ON THE PFD

The amount of instrumentation shown on process flow diagrams differs according to the needs of a particular industry and the policies of a specific company. In principle, instrumentation should be shown only where it effects changes to operating or design conditions and only in a very simplified form. The temperature and pressure control loops of Figure 4-1 are good examples. The level controllers show only one impulse line rather than two.

It is quite permissible to abbreviate instrumentation symbols and identification on process flow diagrams. A single bubble with a single first letter (e.g., P, T, or F) is enough to signal that the variable is of importance to the process. It can be left to later to decide what to do with it (i.e., whether it is to be controlled, measured, or recorded).

The principle to follow is not to commit to a control system design before all the details can be worked out, not to become locked into a system that may have to be modified later. The temperature, pressure, flow, and level loops shown in Figure 4-1 impact operation and should be correct in principle. Flow recorders are of absolutely no consequence to the purpose of the process flow diagram and should be omitted.

▓ SPECIFIC PFD EQUIPMENT SYMBOLS

Process flow diagram equipment symbols can be simpler than engineering flow diagram symbols primarily for two reasons: (1) they are concerned only with the process, not with ancillary details such as control logic or pump drivers; (2) they carry much less specific data than do the detailed engineering flow diagrams.

For these reasons drivers are omitted from drawings; the same symbol is used for centrifugal, centrifugal inline, and canned pumps; and piping arrangements are simplified. These liberties are taken either because the information is not available at the time the PFD is generated or because using the diagram to convey such information would detract from its primary purpose.

Because the symbols used for PFDs are simplified, they are good symbols for control systems drawings. The same principle applies: draw a line only if it is necessary to help convey information that is within the scope of a specific drawing.

In order to simplify discussion and understanding, it is prudent to establish some classification of process equipment. Table 4-1 gives one possible set of categories. Specific examples from each category are given in Figures 4-2 through 4-18, and some will be commented upon.

TABLE 4-1
Equipment Categories by Function

1.0 Mixing, Blending
2.0 Reaction
3.0 Material Separation
4.0 Size Reduction
5.0 Storage
6.0 Transfer Operations
  6.1 Gas Transfer
  6.2 Heat Transfer
  6.3 Liquid Transfer
  6.4 Solids Transfer

Mixing and Blending

Mechanical equipment, such as most of that shown in Figure 4-2, has a tendency to be over-illustrated on drawings. It must be remembered that not machine design but the essential function that the machine performs on the process is of prime importance here. The eight examples shown in Figure 4-2 were chosen because they depict the essentials of mechanical devices without unnecessary redundancy.

It could be argued that the motor symbols are not necessary on the agitator (A) and on the inline mixer (B). Conversely, an argument could be advanced that they are necessary on the drum mixer (B), the helical mixer (C), the ribbon blender (E), and the roll blender (F). The deciding factor is a matter of comfort level, not objectivity. Most people seem to feel that something is missing if the motors are not present on the agitator and the inline mixer; and most seem to think them unnecessary on the rest.

Subtle factors sometimes make large differences. An inclined drum in a sketch of a drum mixer conveys the idea of material flow.

Reaction

The three reactors shown in Figure 4-3 are actually vessels, so reactors or kettles could be lumped together with vessels. However, functionally they differ from storage vessels, so they have been placed in a separate category.

Flow directional arrows and the relative placement of lines are very important. Generally, flow is best established from left to right and from top to bottom. However, gases and vapors usually leave a reactor from the top and can be sparged in from the bottom.

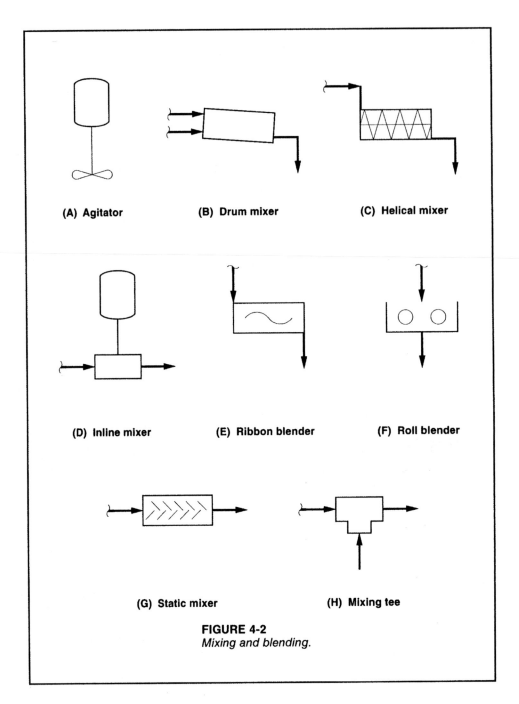

(A) Agitator   (B) Drum mixer   (C) Helical mixer

(D) Inline mixer   (E) Ribbon blender   (F) Roll blender

(G) Static mixer   (H) Mixing tee

FIGURE 4-2
Mixing and blending.

In the case of the jacketed kettle, steam would normally enter the jacket at the top and the condensate should leave at the bottom. The situation might be reversed if the heat transfer fluid were a liquid.

Material Separation

Judging by the number of examples available, material separation is performed more often than any other process in the process industries (see Figures 4-4

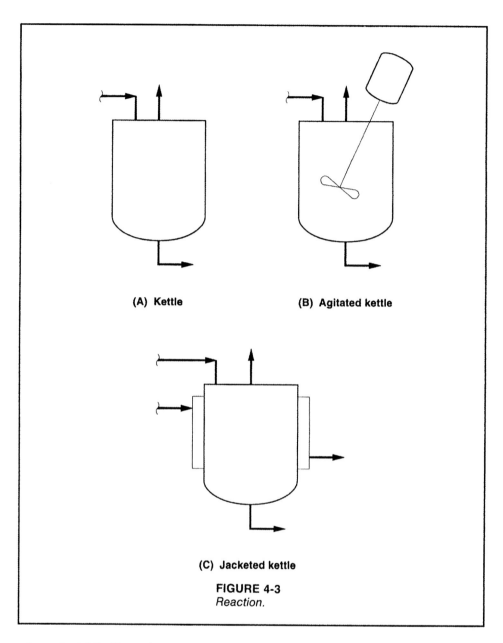

(A) Kettle   (B) Agitated kettle

(C) Jacketed kettle

FIGURE 4-3
Reaction.

through 4-12). Since there are so many categories, Table 4-1 will be used to list the figures. Some of the categories overlap.

This section depicts some of the largest and most complex equipment used in the process industries. Although the equipment may be complex, the PFD uses very few lines to convey information and ideas about it.

Perhaps this is a good place to emphasize the integrity of a drawing. A drawing does not consist of figures alone. Titles, names, notes and data are needed to

TABLE 4-2
Material Separation

(a)	Absorption	(q)	Rotary
(b)	Adsorption	(r)	Rotary Shelf
(c)	Calcining	(s)	Spray
	Centrifugation		Evaporation
(d)	Solid Bowl	(t)	Forced Circulation
(e)	Vertical	(u)	Multiple Effect
(f)	Classifying	(v)	Natural Convection
	Crystallization		Extraction
(g)	Agitated Batch	(w)	Liquid/Liquid
(h)	Vacuum	(x)	Packed Column
(i)	Pachuca		Filtration
(j)	Cycloning	(y)	Bag
	Distillation/Fractionation	(z)	Plate and Frame
(k)	Packed Tower	(aa)	Rotary Vacuum
(l)	Tray Column	(bb)	Precipitation
	Drying		Screening
(m)	Adsorption	(cc)	Vibrating
(n)	Batch	(dd)	Hydro
(o)	Belt	(ee)	Scrubbing
(p)	Drum	(ff)	Settling/Thickening

complete the total picture. For instance, not all columns are identical. Compare the columns of Figures 4-4(A), 4-4(B), 4-6(B), 4-6(C), and 4-10(B). They look alike, but some of them have radically different functions that may be seen clearly only in full context.

Size Reduction

The set of drawings in Figure 4-13 shows that some element of the equipment must serve as the mnemonic essence of a figure. In Figures 4-13(A), (B), and (C), it is the working element: the rolls, the jaws, the cone. In Figures 4-13(D) and (E), it is the external form. Here, the opposite length-to-diameter ratios are characteristic of mills and autogenuous grinders.

Material Storage

Some companies prefer to show all tanks as shown in Figure 4-14(A), without the seam line. This is a question of comfort level.

If it is known at the time of process flow diagram development that a floating roof tank is going to be used, it might as well be depicted as in Figure 4-14 (C).

The storage pile Figure 4-14(G) proves that not all containers have regular sides, which should be remembered.

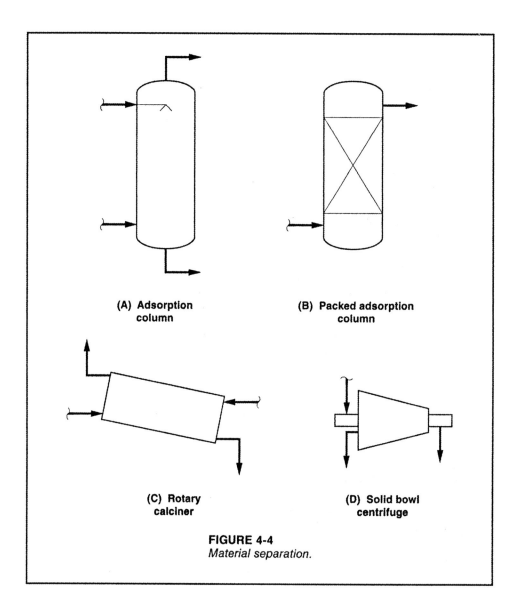

(A) Adsorption
column

(B) Packed adsorption
column

(C) Rotary
calciner

(D) Solid bowl
centrifuge

FIGURE 4-4
Material separation.

Gas Transfer

Comparing the centrifugal compressor in Figure 4-15(A) with the turbine in (B) shows that the same elements, in this case arrows and shapes can be made to mean completely opposite functions when arranged correctly. In (A), compression is taking place; in (B), expansion. Form follows function.

Heat Exchangers

Figure 4-16 shows various types of heat exchangers. There is not a great deal of difference among (A), (B), (C), and (D).

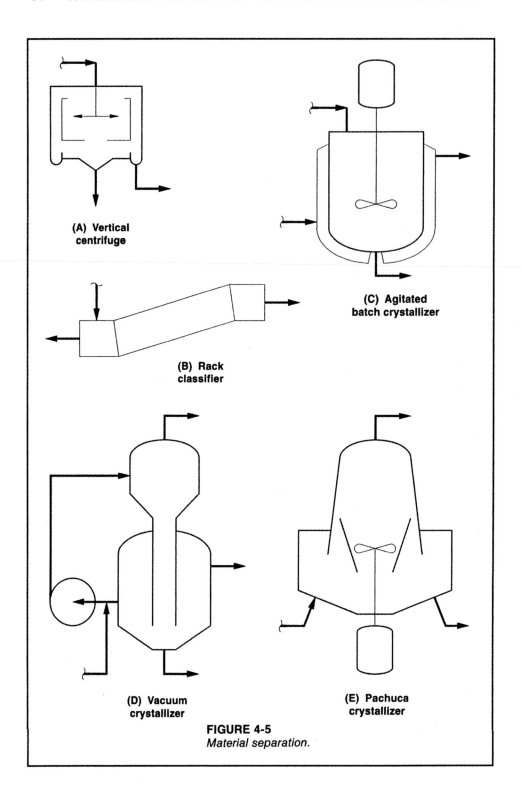

(A) Vertical centrifuge

(B) Rack classifier

(C) Agitated batch crystallizer

(D) Vacuum crystallizer

(E) Pachuca crystallizer

FIGURE 4-5
Material separation.

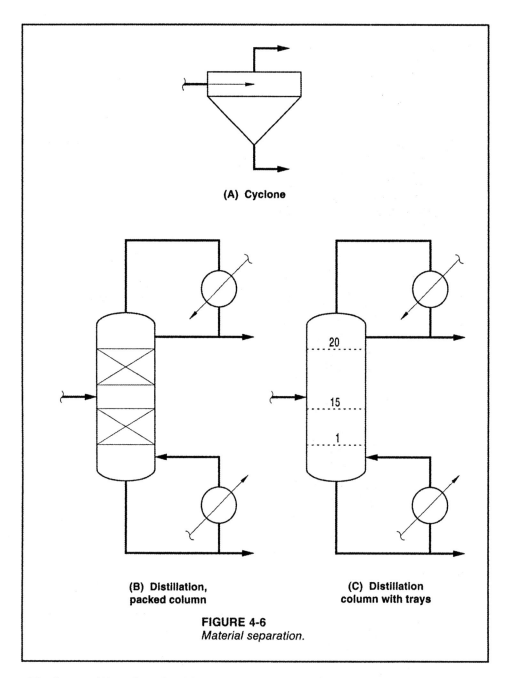

(A) Cyclone

**(B) Distillation,
packed column**

**(C) Distillation
column with trays**

FIGURE 4-6
Material separation.

The heater (A) and cooler (B) are conveniently differentiated by drawing the utility line upwards for a heater and downwards for a cooler. These two are differentiated from the process/process heat exchangers (C) by not continuing the utility lines; they are shown simply as arrows.

All four lines of the process/process heat exchangers Figure 4-16(C) are connected to other equipment. The choice between the two symbols in (C) is simply a drafting convenience to simplify interconnection.

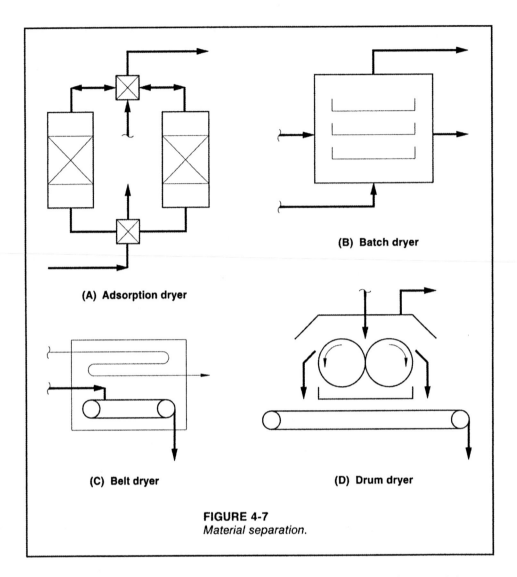

FIGURE 4-7
Material separation.

The symbol for the kettle reboiler Figure 4-16(D) suggests both form and function, as does that for the fin fan cooler (E). The fan does not exist within the process equipment, but placing it there saves drawing space.

Liquid Transfer

Figure 4-17 shows four basic pump symbols. Directional arrows mark the suction and discharge lines. They may be oriented to suit the overall drawing arrangement.

It could be argued that only the general symbol is needed for a PFD. However, when the symbols are used to depict control schemes it is of definite benefit to draw the distinctions, since different control methods must be adopted for each case.

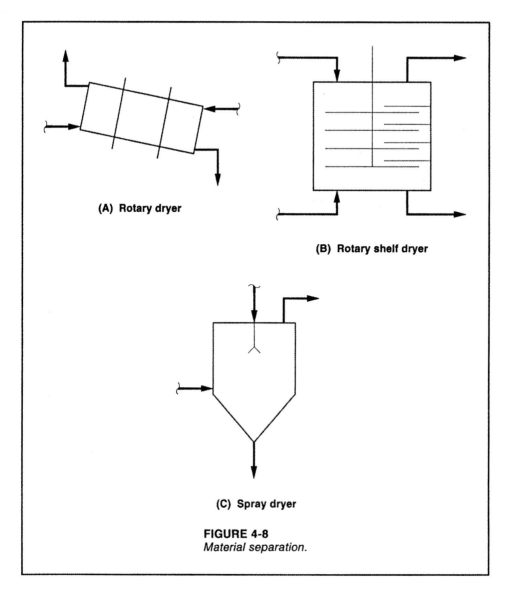

(A) Rotary dryer

(B) Rotary shelf dryer

(C) Spray dryer

FIGURE 4-8
Material separation.

The driver is not shown on a PFD, but it might be on a control systems diagram if it is pertinent to understanding signal flows.

Solids Transfer

A PFD frequently omits material conveying equipment, substituting instead a line with a stream number. But symbols for the equipment have been included; since one of the reasons for showing PFD-type equipment symbols is that they also may be used for process control sketches.

These drawings should be kept simple (see Figure 4-18). It is not necessary to show the drivers, for instance.

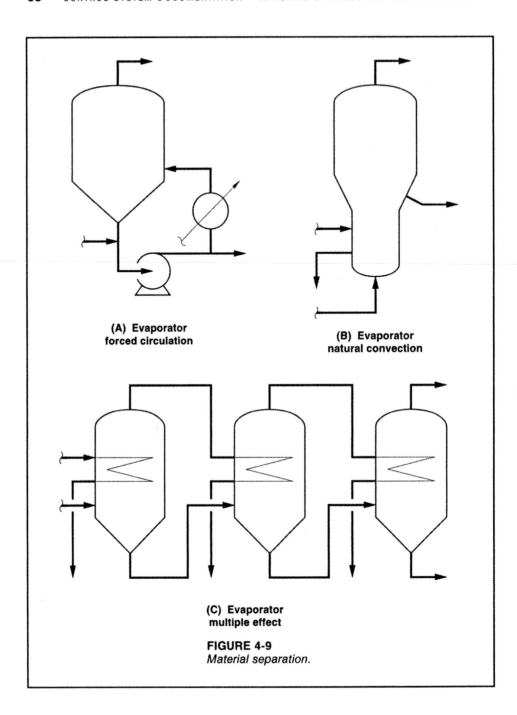

**(A) Evaporator
forced circulation**

**(B) Evaporator
natural convection**

**(C) Evaporator
multiple effect**

FIGURE 4-9
Material separation.

A pneumatic conveyor is not shown because it is nothing more than a pipe, which can be symbolized by a single line. It is the end equipment that supplies the contextual information.

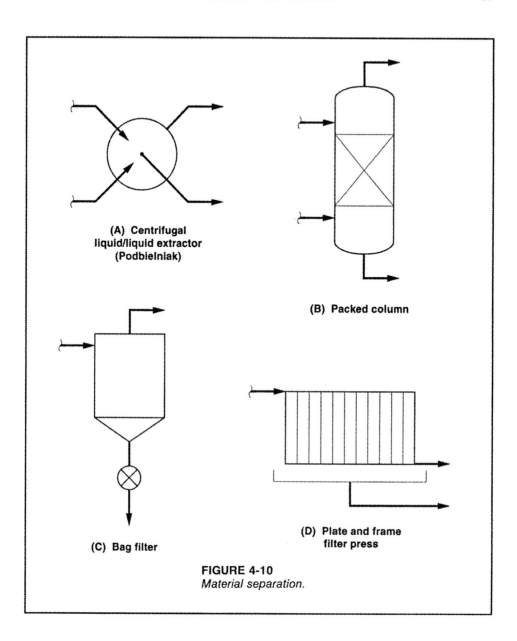

FIGURE 4-10
Material separation.

▨ SUMMARY

The PFD is the springboard for multidisciplinary detailed design. It shows the basic unit operation, major equipment, major piping, and major process flow. The associated material balance and operating or design conditions combined with the drawing itself give the first comprehensive view of the process.

Both the equipment symbols and the instrumentation symbols must be kept simple on the PFD. Equipment symbols and instrumentation symbols are nothing more than mnemonics; they help envision and stabilize thoughts.

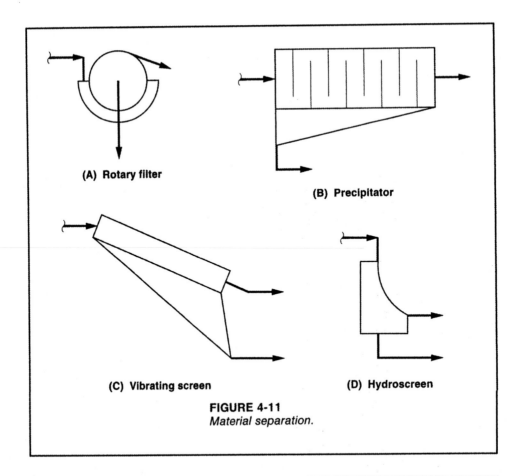

(A) Rotary filter

(B) Precipitator

(C) Vibrating screen

(D) Hydroscreen

FIGURE 4-11
Material separation.

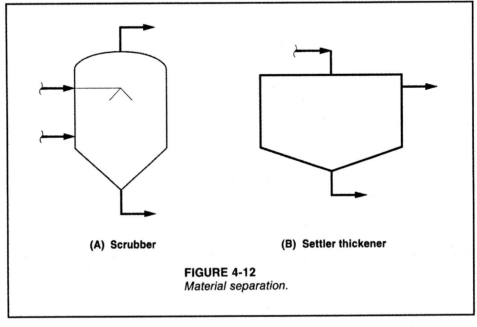

(A) Scrubber

(B) Settler thickener

FIGURE 4-12
Material separation.

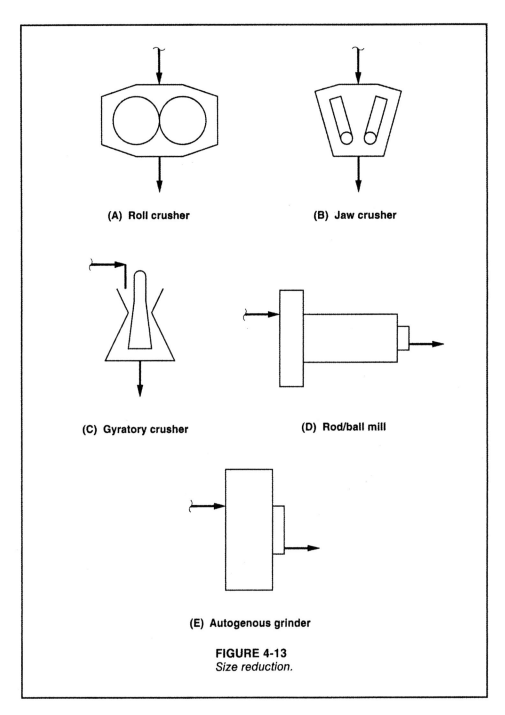

(A) Roll crusher

(B) Jaw crusher

(C) Gyratory crusher

(D) Rod/ball mill

(E) Autogenous grinder

FIGURE 4-13
Size reduction.

Poorly chosen, cluttered symbols usually clashes with the aesthetic sensibilities of the beholder and detracts from clear thinking.

Instrumentation symbols on a PFD should be abbreviated in the extreme. It is too early in the design process to get into details. Therefore, it is permissible to

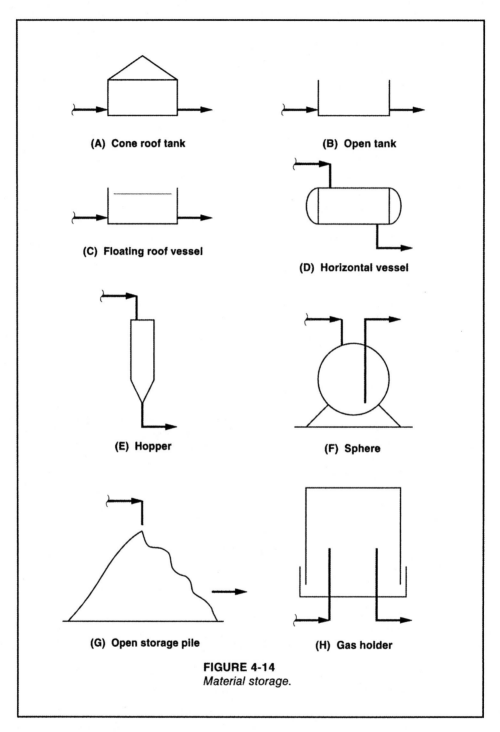

(A) Cone roof tank

(B) Open tank

(C) Floating roof vessel

(D) Horizontal vessel

(E) Hopper

(F) Sphere

(G) Open storage pile

(H) Gas holder

FIGURE 4-14
Material storage.

omit primary elements, transmitters, alarms, and such ancillaries as square root extractors. The sole purpose of showing any instrumentation on a PFD is to signal the importance of a variable for measurement or control—not to explain how it is to be done. This is the task of detailed engineering.

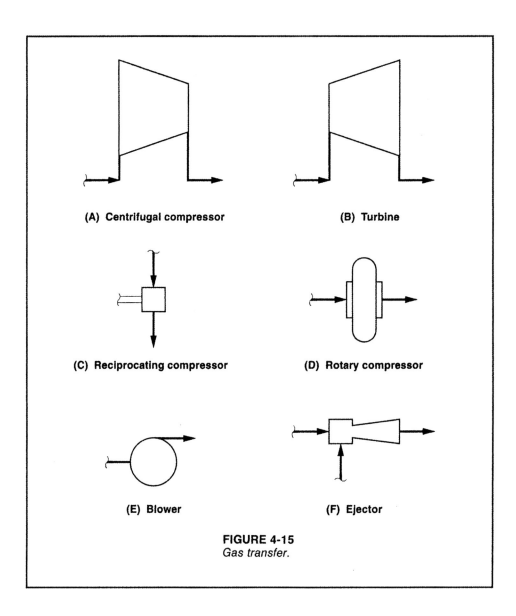

FIGURE 4-15
Gas transfer.

Equipment symbols used on PFDs are also of importance to control systems engineers because they are ideal for control systems drawings. These drawings and sketches emphasize the details of instrument loops and de-emphasize equipment details. It is because of the utility of PFD-type equipment symbols to the control systems engineer that so many examples are given. The examples are by no means all inclusive. However, they represent a good cross section of what the control systems engineer deals with in the process industries.

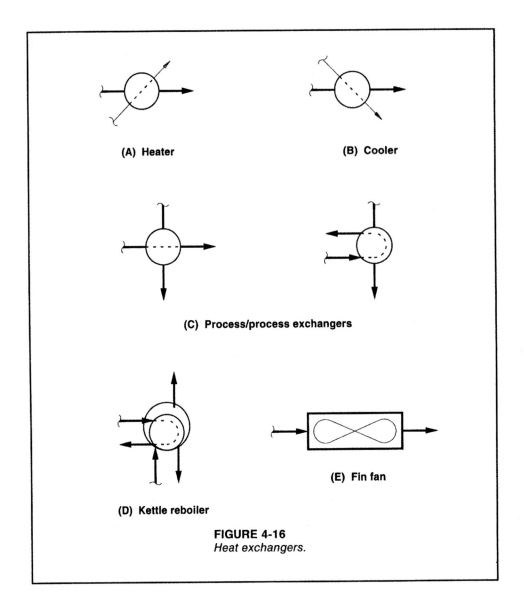

(A) Heater

(B) Cooler

(C) Process/process exchangers

(D) Kettle reboiler

(E) Fin fan

FIGURE 4-16
Heat exchangers.

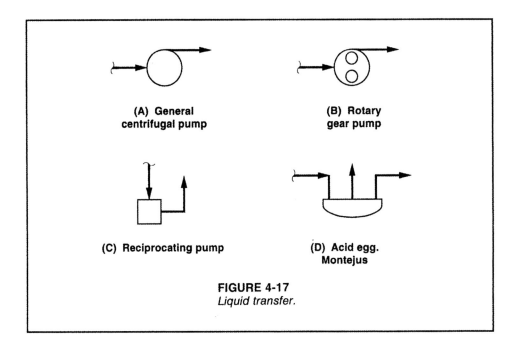

(A) General
centrifugal pump

(B) Rotary
gear pump

(C) Reciprocating pump

(D) Acid egg.
Montejus

FIGURE 4-17
Liquid transfer.

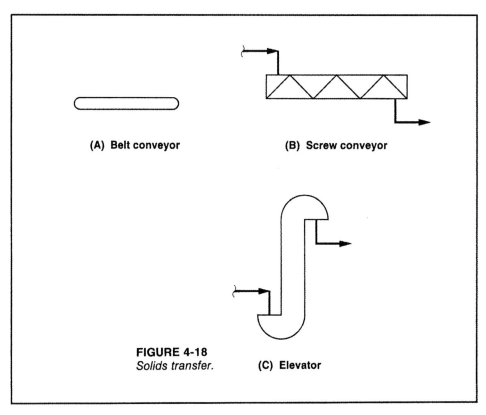

(A) Belt conveyor

(B) Screw conveyor

FIGURE 4-18
Solids transfer.

(C) Elevator

▨ QUESTIONS

1. What is the primary purpose of a Process Flow Diagram (PFD)?

2. Who develops the PFD?

3. Of what use is it to the control systems engineer?

4. The PFD is a precursor to another major engineering drawing. Name this drawing.

5. What is the purpose of showing instrument symbols on a PFD?

6. Why are simplified symbols and identification used on a PFD in your opinion?

7. Are all measured and controlled variables shown on a PFD? If not, why not?

8. Why must control systems personnel not miss the opportunity to influence the development of the PFD?

9. What defines the extent of the process to be depicted on a PFD?

10. Why are PFD equipment symbols and identification suitable for developing control systems sketches and drawings?

11. How do you decide what to include and what to exclude from equipment symbols? Are the rules hard and fast?

12. Think about the examples given under the various categories of equipment symbols and decide whether or not you agree with the choices. If you do not agree, sketch a different example.

13. Why is it important to know whether information on a PFD represents design conditions or operating conditions?

5

STRUCTURED CONTROL CONCEPTS

▓ INTRODUCTION: PUTTING THE BUILDING BLOCKS TOGETHER

Between the process flow diagram (PFD) and the engineering flow diagram (EFD) lies much control systems thought, which may or may not find itself represented on a formal design document. The PFD formally represents the basic process; the EFD (also called the process or piping and instrumentation diagram or P&ID) formally represents the detailed design of the process equipment and its interconnections. It is a more or less complete shopping list. Control system representation on the P&ID varies in completeness from company to company and, indeed, from project to project.

Whether or not the above-mentioned control systems thought is formally documented, it must be schematized if a workable control system is to be developed and procured. This chapter is concerned with symbolizing structured control concepts that can serve as building blocks to a complete design.

Ed Bristol of the Foxboro Company has attempted to formalize the design process in a paper that he presented on what he calls "idiomatic control" [Ref. 1]. Bristol describes idioms as mini-inventions in the control system designer's bag of tricks that have been built up over years of experience in solving similar problems. When a new problem arises, the designer reaches into his or her bag of tricks, pulls out an idiom, modifies it to suit the problem context, and uses it.

The parallel between idiomatic language and structured control concepts is very good. People think and talk in idioms, and idioms used out of context are meaningless or misleading. Engineers design in terms of structured control concepts, and structured control concepts when misapplied can be disastrous. However, the author prefers not to use the term "idiomatic control" since this

TABLE 5-1
Structured Control Concepts

A. LINEAR CONTINUOUS CONTROLS

    1. FEEDBACK CONTROL
    2. FEEDFORWARD CONTROL
    3. DECOUPLING
    4. CASCADE CONTROL
    5. RATIO CONTROL

B. MULTIPLE OUTPUT CONTROL

    1. LOAD BALANCING
    2. RANGE EXTENDING

C. REDUNDANT LOOPS

    1. REDUNDANT BACKUP
    2. INTEGRAL LOOP TAKEOVER
    3. VALVE POSITION CONTROL

D. SWITCHED CONTROLS

    1. AUCTIONEERING
    2. SELECTOR SYSTEMS
    3. VARIABLE STRUCTURE

chapter addresses control concepts rather than direct control per se. Therefore, we shall employ the more generic description, "structured control concepts."

However, Bristol's outline of categories will be followed. As he points out, the categories are not complete, but they are a good starting point and representative symbolism for each element will be provided. Since this is a text on symbolism and identification, not design, the reader is cautioned to thoroughly understand the basic concepts before applying them. Table 5-1 outlines Bristol's categories.

The remainder of this chapter will deal with the problem of symbolizing structured control concepts. Symbolic depictions of each of Bristol's categories will be shown along with appropriate commentary.

STRUCTURED CONTROL CONCEPT NUMBER ONE: FEEDBACK CONTROL

The purpose of feedback control is to control a measured variable at a set point. The set point is not always apparent, nor easily adjustable [the spring adjustment on self-contained regulators, for instance; see Figures 5-1(A) and (B)].

The operational states are auto and manual. The operational parameters are the set point (in auto) and the output (in manual, Figure 5-1(C) only).

Monitored values are the set point, the measurement, and the output. It is to be noted that "monitored" is not necessarily synonymous with "displayed."

It should be apparent from the figure that this is a concept rather than a means or a method. The concept is feedback control. A set point is being generated, a measured variable is compared with the set point, and an output results. The output may change a controlled variable, which can alter the measured variable. The state of the measured variable is fed back to the controller for further comparison and change, if necessary.

Briefly, this is the essence of feedback control. It is irrelevant that there are five elements in the flow loop [Figure 5-1(C)] versus only one for the pressure control valves (PCVs) [Figures 5-1(A) and (B)] or that the PCVs are self-contained mechanical devices with no displays or adjustments while flow loops can be complex electronic systems. It is also irrelevant that the manipulated and measured variables are identical in the flow loop but not in the pressure loop. The structured control concept is feedback control, not the means or method of obtaining it.

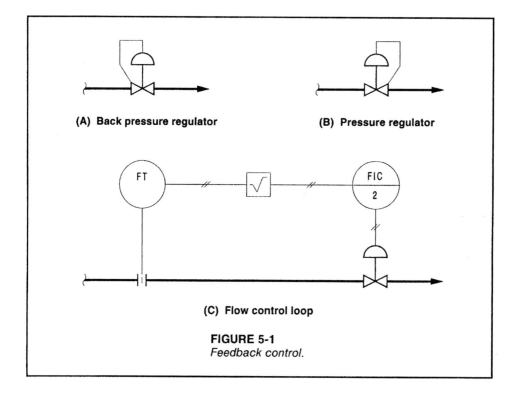

(A) **Back pressure regulator**   (B) **Pressure regulator**

(C) **Flow control loop**

FIGURE 5-1
Feedback control.

▨ STRUCTURED CONTROL CONCEPT NUMBER TWO: FEEDFORWARD CONTROL

The purpose of feedforward control is to obviate the effects of load disturbances.

Figure 5-2 is a generalized schematic of the concept [Ref. 2]. The load components are material and energy flows whose changes tend to change the controlled variable, c. In order to counteract these tendencies, the load changes are measured, fed to a feedforward system that calculates their influence against a set point and adjusts a manipulated variable that affects the process in such a way as to minimize the deviation from set point.

Figure 5-3 is an example of a pure feedforward scheme [Ref. 2] to control the discharge temperature, T2, on the process side of a steam-heated exchanger. The feedforward portion of the loop is blocked out for clarity. This portion calculates the required steam flow, Ws, given a measured process flow, Wp, process temperature to the exchanger, Tl, and desired process temperature, T2, supplied by the hand control, HC. The steam flow control loop is a standard feedback loop. It is a cascaded loop whose function is to improve the accuracy of the system.

Figure 5-4 shows a standard three-element boiler feedwater control system. The example is given to emphasize the importance of having clear concepts. The feedforward portion is blocked out. Even though this portion is on the

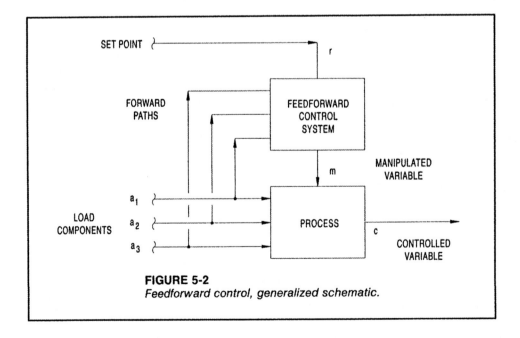

FIGURE 5-2
Feedforward control, generalized schematic.

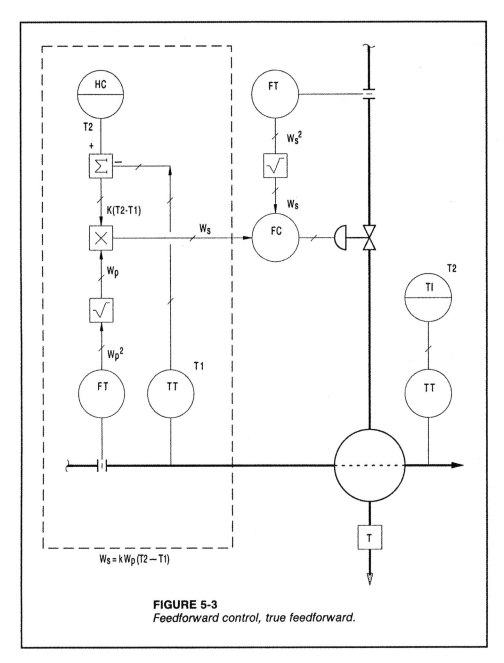

FIGURE 5-3
Feedforward control, true feedforward.

discharge (downstream) side of the boiler, it is still feedforward, since feedforward deals with process disturbances wherever they occur.

The purpose of this particular feedforward loop is to calculate the feedwater flow necessary to match the steam demand, the load (also a disturbance). The purpose of the level control loop is to trim the calculation so that level remains close to optimum for boiler efficiency and safety. The level control loop is a feedback loop cascaded into the feedwater flow control loop. The purpose of

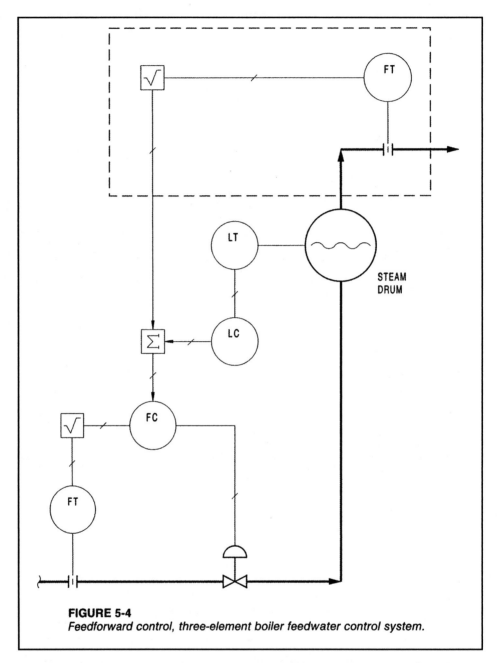

FIGURE 5-4
Feedforward control, three-element boiler feedwater control system.

the feedwater flow control loop is to improve the accuracy of response to the calculated and trimmed set point signal. It is also a feedback loop.

The operational state is normally automatic. However, for failed inputs, a fixed input may be entered manually under some circumstances. Operational parameters are the set point and, sometimes, substituted inputs (for failed systems).

Monitored values are measured inputs and calculated output(s).

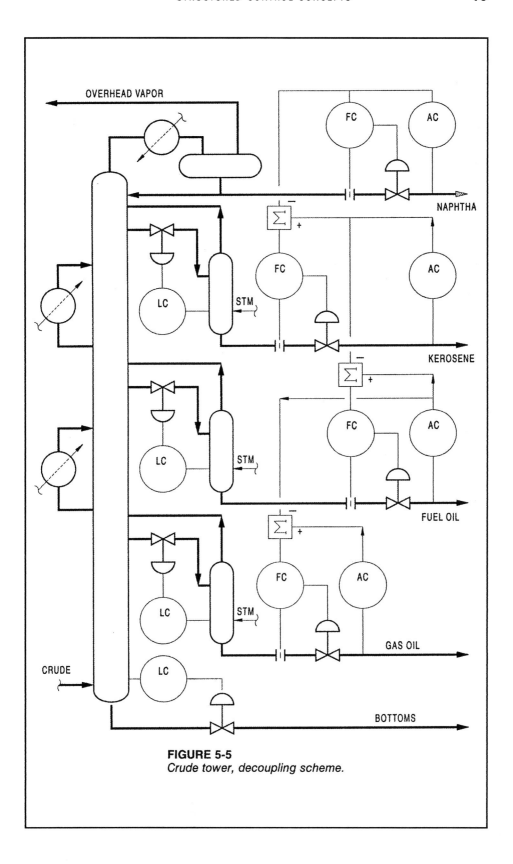

FIGURE 5-5
Crude tower, decoupling scheme.

▨ STRUCTURED CONTROL CONCEPT NUMBER THREE: DECOUPLING

The purpose of decoupling is to reduce interaction in multiloop, multivariable situations.

Figure 5-5 was chosen because it allows an intuitive grasp of the interaction and its compensation. The decoupling signals are the negative inputs to the summers. If the naphtha analyzer demands more flow through the top sidestream, the vapor/liquid ratio will increase, increasing the heavier components in the top sidestream to achieve set point. Heavier components will also find their way into the kerosene sidestream unless this sidestream's flow is reduced to allow more stripping in the sidestream stripper.

For a mathematical analysis the reader is referred to Ref.3.

The operational states are automatic with one, possibly, in which the decoupling signal is switched out. Operational parameters are set points and outputs.

Monitored values are the measured and the manipulated (for tuning) variables.

▨ STRUCTURED CONTROL CONCEPT NUMBER FOUR: CASCADE CONTROL

Cascade control allows a primary controller to trim a secondary one, thus improving control by speeding response and reducing disturbances caused by the secondary loop.

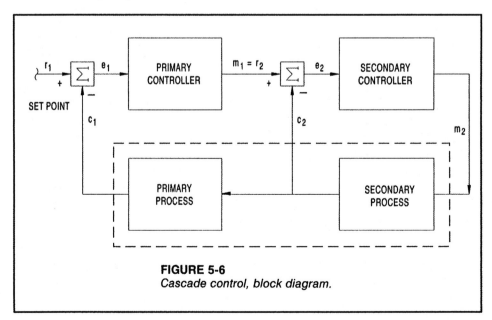

FIGURE 5-6
Cascade control, block diagram.

Figure 5-6 is a block diagram of the concept. It shows the process broken into primary and secondary portions. The summers represent the error signal generators. A cascade is characterized by the fact that $m_1 = r_2$: the output (manipulated variable) of the primary loop sets (cascades into) the set point of the secondary loop.

Figure 5-7 is a particular example of cascade control with the corresponding manipulated and controlled variables designated. It is noteworthy that the set points and internal error signals are not symbolized when a schematic becomes more specific. It is also noteworthy that simple schematics sometimes hide complex phenomena. For instance, the depiction is of an exothermic reaction.

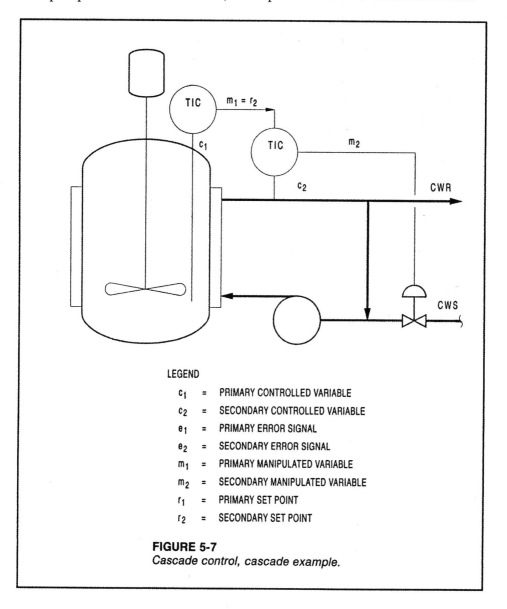

LEGEND

c_1	=	PRIMARY CONTROLLED VARIABLE
c_2	=	SECONDARY CONTROLLED VARIABLE
e_1	=	PRIMARY ERROR SIGNAL
e_2	=	SECONDARY ERROR SIGNAL
m_1	=	PRIMARY MANIPULATED VARIABLE
m_2	=	SECONDARY MANIPULATED VARIABLE
r_1	=	PRIMARY SET POINT
r_2	=	SECONDARY SET POINT

FIGURE 5-7
Cascade control, cascade example.

■ STRUCTURED CONTROL CONCEPTS NUMBER FIVE: RATIO CONTROL

The purpose of ratio control is to control blends or stoichiometric quantities in proportion to one another.

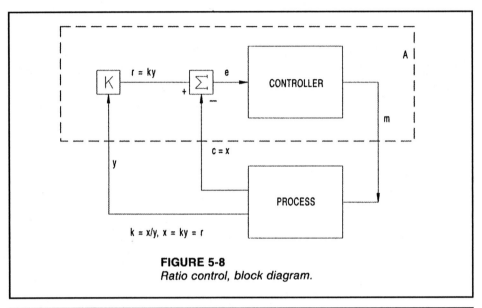

FIGURE 5-8
Ratio control, block diagram.

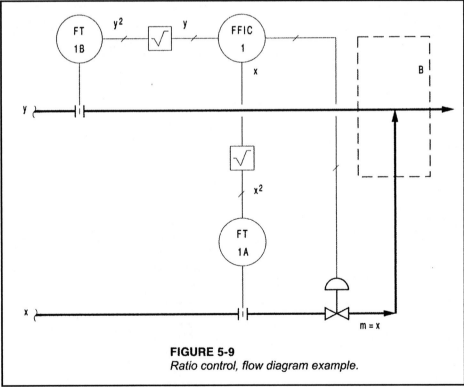

FIGURE 5-9
Ratio control, flow diagram example.

Blending is a common form of ratio control. Figure 5-8 is a block diagram of the ratio control concept. The algebra is performed outside the closed loop to avoid gain problems (see Ref. 4 for an explanation). Figure 5-9 is a more common control-oriented diagram. In order to aid understanding, block A in Figure 5-8 corresponds to the FFIC in Figure 5-9, and block B in Figure 5-9 corresponds to the process block in Figure 5-8.

The operational states depend upon the application. Sometimes, when there are multiple loops, some loops may be taken out of the ratio mode and operated independently. In pacing loops, often the ratio will be maintained regardless of which loop is in manual. The operational parameters are also highly application dependent.

The monitored values are the ratio set point and its measured value together with the measured values associated with each controller in the loop.

▨ STRUCTURED CONTROL CONCEPT NUMBER SIX: LOAD BALANCING

The purpose of load balancing is to permit regulation of the common (summed) output of several loops. Figure 5-10 is typical.

The operational states are any combination of the normal operational states of the individual loops. Any of the individual loops may be in the manual mode and the outer loop will still attempt to maintain the total flow at its (the outer loop's) set point. The operational parameters are those of all the controllers including the outer load balancing controller. (This does not mean to say that all combinations are useful.) The monitored values also are those associated with each individual controller and with the load balancing controller.

▨ STRUCTURED CONTROL CONCEPT NUMBER SEVEN: RANGE EXTENDING

The purpose of range extending is to increase the normal range of an element over what would normally be available. The example of Figure 5-11 shows two valves in parallel. FV-A is stroked fully before FV-B starts to modulate. FV-A remains fully open as long as the system is in the range of FV-B. The operational states as well as the operational parameters are those of a control element with a single final element. The monitored values are also those of an individual control element but could be extended to include the individual signals. Positioners are necessary but are not shown.

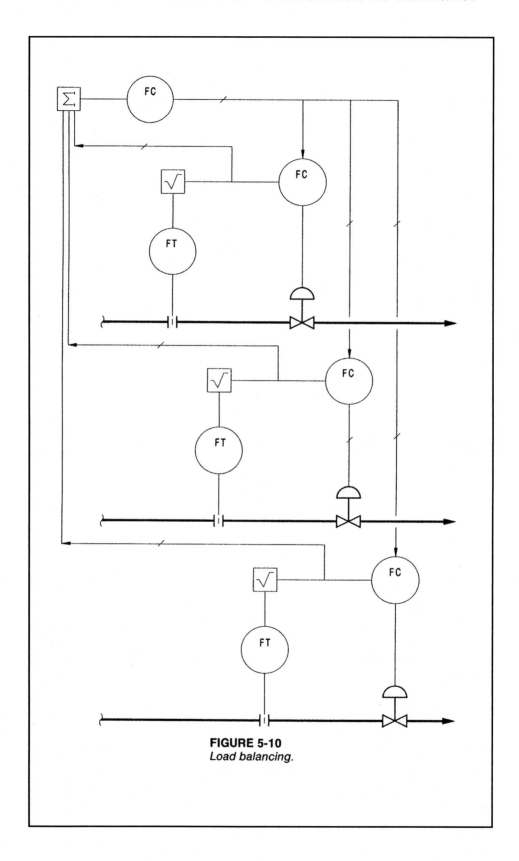

FIGURE 5-10
Load balancing.

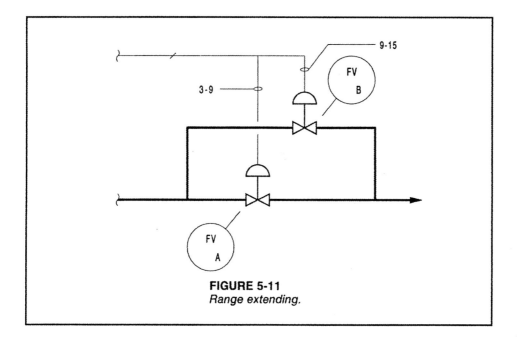

FIGURE 5-11
Range extending.

▨ STRUCTURED CONTROL CONCEPT NUMBER EIGHT: REDUNDANT LOOPS

Redundant loops appear in many different forms, a few of which are presented here. Backup is an obvious form of redundancy. The simplest form of backup is shown in Figure 5-12. Backpressure controllers are basically narrow band proportional-only controllers. If they have different set points, they will open at different times.

Figure 5-13 shows a similar but more complicated form of the same concept.

Figure 5-14 shows a variation on the same theme. If one controller is proportional-only and the other has reset, the response changes. Loop 2, the proportional-only loop, becomes the fast loop. Loop 1, the slow loop, will move to gradually eliminate its error due to its integral action.

Figure 5-15 is what Shinskey [Ref. 5] refers to as "valve position control" and, unfortunately, VPC has been used to designate the controller. This is not necessary, according to ISA-5.1 [Ref. 6]. Since the second (fast) controller is associated with a different variable, it deserves a different loop number. The choice is between the unclassified variable, X, or one of the user's choice variables. The purpose of the loop is to have a larger, slower-acting valve and a smaller, faster-acting valve.

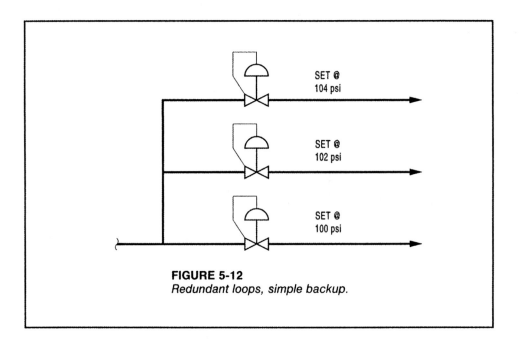

FIGURE 5-12
Redundant loops, simple backup.

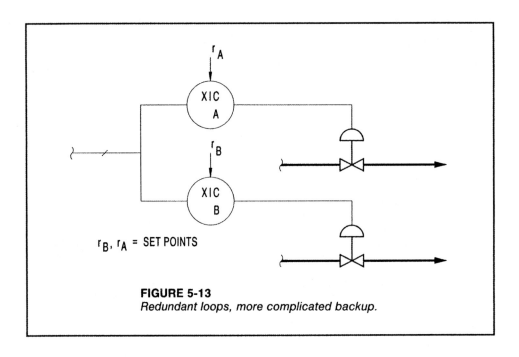

FIGURE 5-13
Redundant loops, more complicated backup.

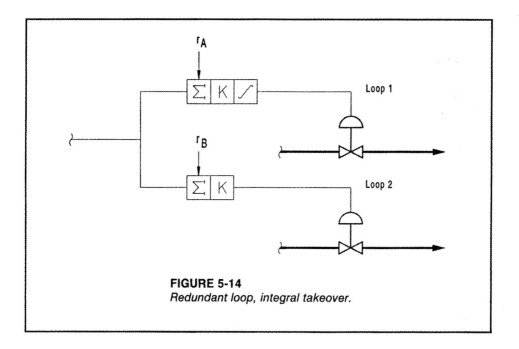

FIGURE 5-14
Redundant loop, integral takeover.

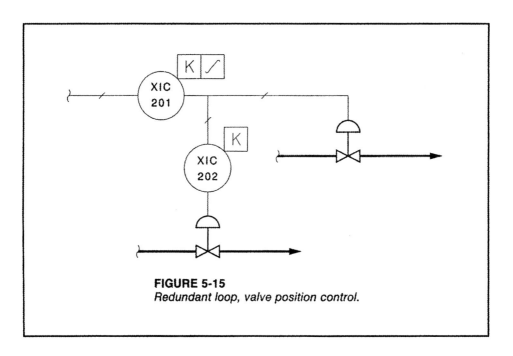

FIGURE 5-15
Redundant loop, valve position control.

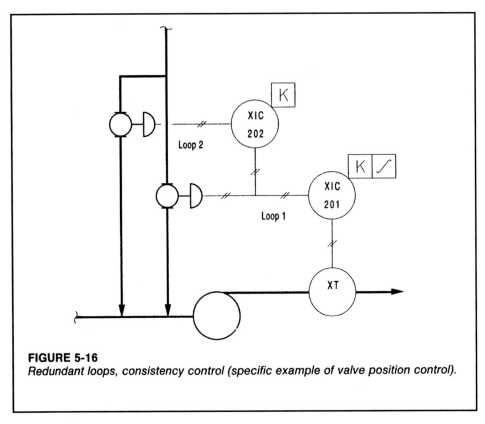

FIGURE 5-16
Redundant loops, consistency control (specific example of valve position control).

Figure 5-16 is a specific example of consistency control in a pulp and paper mill. Whitewater and pulp are brought into the pump suction. The pump acts as a good mixer. Large quantities are involved, and the pulp flow to the pump may be erratic. To steady out the changes, the fast-acting controller of Loop 2 tries to keep the slower controller of Loop 1 modulating around a mean value.

■ STRUCTURED CONTROL CONCEPT NUMBER NINE: SWITCHED CONTROLS

Switched control concepts are divided into auctioneering, high (or low) selection, and variable structure.

Auctioneering, Figure 5-17, involves switching on the input side of the controller, which is one method of overcoming the problem of less than adequate analyzers: if one fails, the other takes over.

High selection, Figure 5-18, involves two separate controllers with the switching on the output. External feedback is necessary since one of the controllers would be wound up most of the time if external feedback were not used.

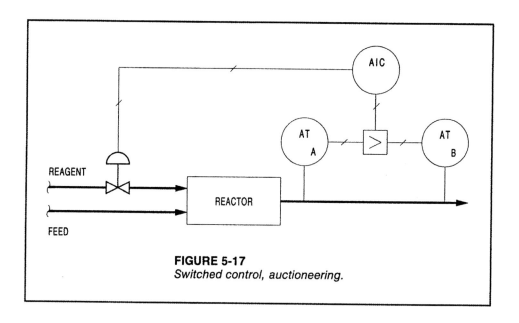

FIGURE 5-17
Switched control, auctioneering.

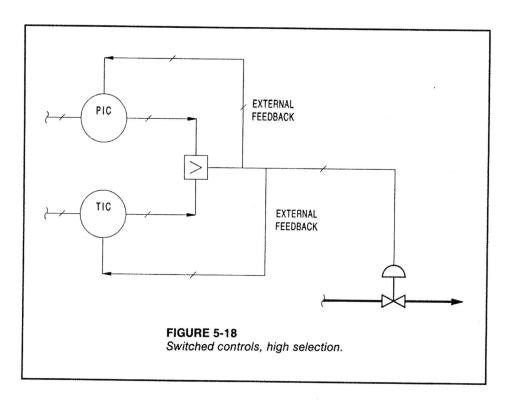

FIGURE 5-18
Switched controls, high selection.

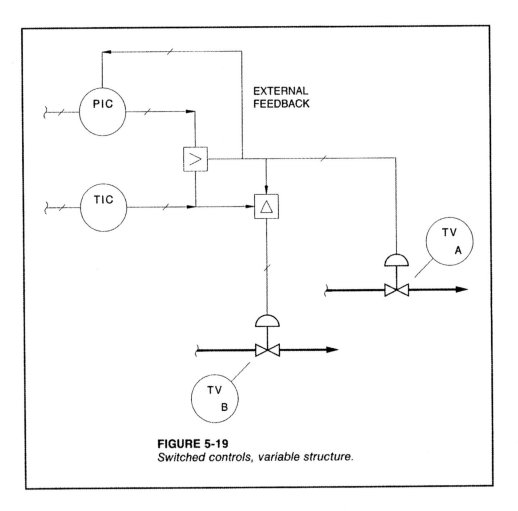

FIGURE 5-19
Switched controls, variable structure.

Variable structure, Figure 5-19, depicts an interesting variation. It allows the TIC to control the process with one valve, TV-A, until a pressure constraint is reached. Then the pressure controller takes over control of the main valve, and the temperature controller takes over the secondary valve, TV-B. External feedback is necessary on the PIC, since it is a dormant loop until called upon. It is not necessary on the TIC, since this loop is always active.

▓ SUMMARY

This chapter attempts to symbolize some of the basic concepts used in control systems work. It shows that these concepts can be used as building blocks in the further development of control systems.

Ed Bristol's categories [Ref. 1] are used as a basis. These categories are not all-inclusive.

▨ QUESTIONS

1. Why was this chapter placed between the one describing PFDs and that describing engineering flow diagrams (EFDs)?

2. Is it true that we think and talk in idioms?

3. Why are Bristol's control categories useful to the designer? Do they all form part of your intellectual bag of tricks?

4. Describe in your own words the essence of the following structured control concepts:

    - feed forward control;
    - feedback control;
    - decoupling;
    - cascade control;
    - ratio control;
    - load balancing;
    - range extending;
    - redundant loops;
    - the three switched controls.

REFERENCES

1. Bristol, E. H., 1981. *After DDC: Idiomatic (Structured) Control* The Foxboro Company, Foxboro, MA. (Paper Given at Seminar: Applications of Advanced Control in the Chemical Process Industries. University of Maryland, May 11-15, 1981.)

2. Shinskey, F. G., 1996. *Process Control Systems: Applications, Design, and Tuning*, Fourth Edition, New York, McGraw-Hill Book Company.

3. McAvoy, T. J., 1983. *Interaction Analysis: Principles and Applications*. Research Triangle Park: Instrument Society of America.

4. Buckley, P. S., 1976. *Design of Pneumatic Flow Controls. Proceedings Thirty-first Annual Symposium on Instrumentation for the Process Industries*, Texas A & M University.

5. Shinskey, F. G., 1981. *Controlling Multivariable Processes*. Research Triangle Park: Instrument Society of America.

6. ISA-5.1-1984(R1992), Instrumentation Symbols and Identification.

THE ENGINEERING FLOW DIAGRAM

▨ INTRODUCTION: DETAILED FLOW SHEETS

The engineering flow diagram (EFD) is a more or less complete shopping list that represents piping, equipment, and instrumentation for a given process. Although it is treated as a design document, it is, in fact, the culmination of the design effort from a process engineer's point of view. In effect, many designs are finally brought together and represented formally on the engineering flow diagram. They do not necessarily originate with the engineering flow diagram.

There are almost as many styles of engineering flow diagrams as there are engineering companies. Instrumentation, in particular, is variously represented. It ranges from highly simplified depictions to detailed ones. There is no perfect style. However, there are objective guidelines that, when followed, lead to a good and efficient design. This chapter will attempt to offer some guidelines with an emphasis on control systems.

Legend Sheet

Even if there is only one engineering flow diagram, a legend sheet is imperative (Figure 6-1). A legend sheet lets the reader know what might not be evident from a common sense point of view, for instance, whether a blocked-in valve symbol means globe valve or needle valve. It defines the use of symbols. This definition is mandatory, since the same symbol is often used by different companies to represent different concepts.

The legend sheet is usually a full-sized sheet, or a full frame, in tabular format, which carries the principal symbols, identification, and other pertinent information that will be used in a repetitive fashion on the detailed flow sheets that are associated with a particular project. The information is usually organized in titled, tabular blocks. Instrumentation identification and symbols that figure predominantly on a legend sheet are usually taken directly from ISA-5.1 [Ref. 1].

The legend sheet is the location at which the alternate choices given in ISA-5.1 must be made specific. The legend sheet is an opportunity to define specifically what symbols will be used throughout a project. For instance, the dashed electrical line symbol may be chosen over the triple-hatched one, and specific piping symbols, which may have meaning only to one process plant, will be defined.

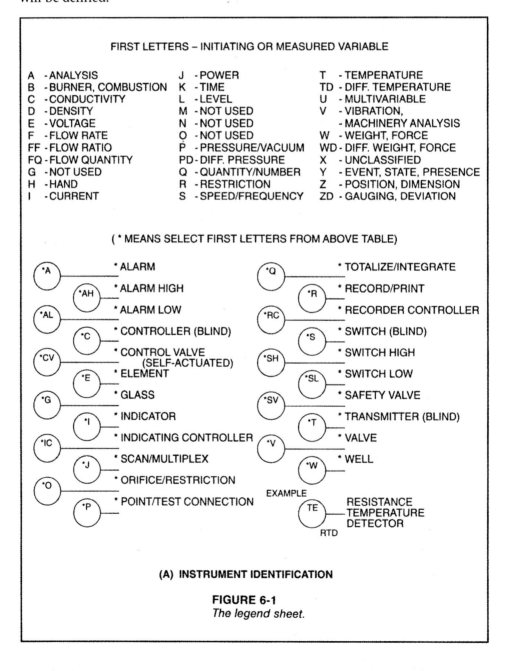

FIGURE 6-1
The legend sheet.

ATM	- ATMOSPHERE	kW	- KILOWATT
AG	- ABOVE GROUND	LC	- LOCKED CLOSED
BCFC	- BROMOCHLORO-DIFLUORO-METHANE	LIL	- LOW INTERFACE LEVEL
BD	- BLOWDOWN	LLL	- LOW LIQUID LEVEL
BL	- BATTERY LIMITS	LO	- LOCKED OPEN
C	- CHEMICAL DRAIN	LP	- LOW PRESSURE
CA	- CORROSION ALLOWANCE	NC	- NORMALLY CLOSED
CO	- CHAIN OPERATED	NIL	- NORMAL INTERFACE LEVEL
CSC	- CAR SEALED CLOSED	NLL	- NORMAL LIQUID LEVEL
CSO	- CAR SEALED OPEN	NO	- NORMALLY OPEN
CW	- COOLING WATER	O	- OILY WATER DRAIN
CWR	- COOLING WATER RETURN	OWS	- OILY WATER SEWER
CWS	- COOLING WATER SUPPLY	PO	- PUMP OUT
(F)	- VENDOR FURNISHED	RO	- RESTRICTION ORIFICE
(F&P)	- VENDOR FURNISHED AND PIPED	S	- STORM WATER DRAIN
FC	- FAIL CLOSED	SC	- SAMPLE CONNECTION
FI	- FAIL IN INTERMEDIATE POSITION	SD	- SHUT DOWN
FL	- FAIL LOCKED	SO	- STEAM OUT
FO	- FAIL OPEN	SP	- SET POINT
FP	- FULL PORT	SG	- SPECIFIC GRAVITY
GO	- GEAR OPERATED	SSV	- SAFETY SHUTDOWN VALVE
HIL	- HIGH INTERFACE LEVEL	TSO	- TIGHT SHUTOFF
HLL	- HIGH LIQUID LEVEL	T/T	- TANGENT TO TANGENT
HOA	- HAND-OFF-AUTO	VB	- VORTEX BREAKER
HP	- HIGH PRESSURE	UG	- UNDER GROUND
IAS	- INSTRUMENT AIR SUPPLY	US	- UTILITY STATION
Ic	- INSULATION (COLD)		
Ih	- INSULATION (HOT)		
Is	- INSULATION (SAFETY)		

(B) ABBREVIATIONS

FIGURE 6-1 (cont.)

The examples of Figure 6-1 are portions of a typical legend sheet. The table in Figure 6-1(A), gives the measured or initiating variable associated with first-letters. Please note that the choices given in ISA-5.1 become specific in this table and that where a users' choice letter is not to be used on a project, it is so stated. Should the need arise later for a new users' choice variable, the legend will be revised and reissued.

The table usually will be followed by some means of depicting the uses of the succeeding-letters, either in tabular or in symbolic form. Note that the legend sheet is a single sheet or frame, so it cannot carry all the information contained in ISA-5.1.

Another block [Figure 6-1(B)] is used to define an extensive list of abbreviations. This is an important reference, given the variation in local practices. The abbreviations are frequently broken down into equipment codes, process codes, and utility codes. They are used subsequently to avoid the use of long designations on the actual flow sheets.

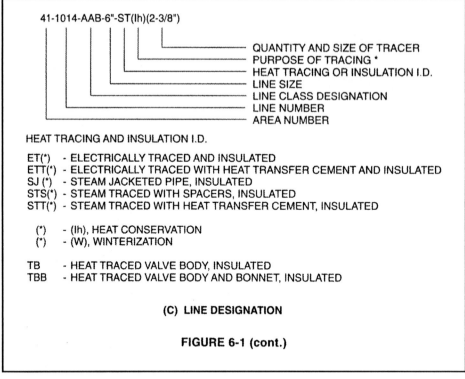

HEAT TRACING AND INSULATION I.D.

ET(*)   - ELECTRICALLY TRACED AND INSULATED
ETT(*) - ELECTRICALLY TRACED WITH HEAT TRANSFER CEMENT AND INSULATED
SJ (*)   - STEAM JACKETED PIPE, INSULATED
STS(*) - STEAM TRACED WITH SPACERS, INSULATED
STT(*) - STEAM TRACED WITH HEAT TRANSFER CEMENT, INSULATED

  (*)   - (lh), HEAT CONSERVATION
  (*)   - (W), WINTERIZATION

TB   - HEAT TRACED VALVE BODY, INSULATED
TBB   - HEAT TRACED VALVE BODY AND BONNET, INSULATED

(C) LINE DESIGNATION

FIGURE 6-1 (cont.)

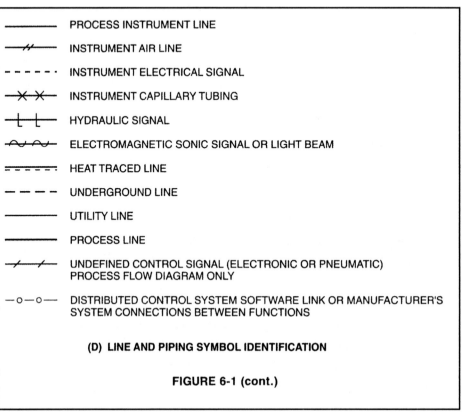

(D) LINE AND PIPING SYMBOL IDENTIFICATION

FIGURE 6-1 (cont.)

There is frequently a list of area numbers, especially in petroleum refining practice.

A line designation legend [Figure 6-1(C)] gives the coding associated with different piping and ducting lines. It includes such codes as line numbers, line schedules, line insulation type, and whether or not a line is traced.

Symbols that identify line and piping [Figure 6-1(D)] also show the meaning of line weights and types.

Also included on the legend sheet is a block for control valve symbols [Figure 6-1(E)], one for manual valve symbols [Figure 6-1(F)], and one for miscellaneous devices such as safety devices, inline devices, and various piping components that will be symbolized later [Figure 6-1(G)].

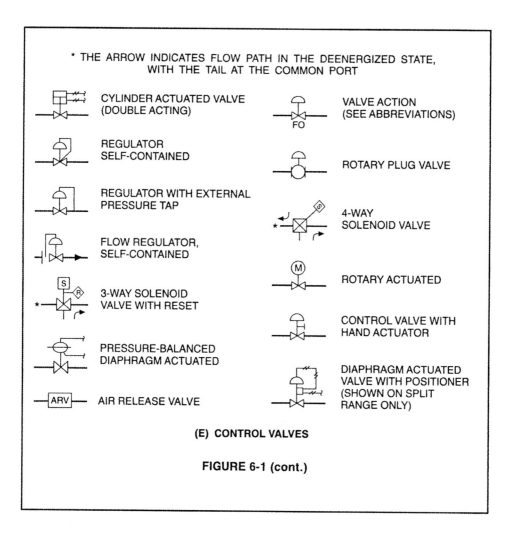

* THE ARROW INDICATES FLOW PATH IN THE DEENERGIZED STATE, WITH THE TAIL AT THE COMMON PORT

CYLINDER ACTUATED VALVE (DOUBLE ACTING)

REGULATOR SELF-CONTAINED

REGULATOR WITH EXTERNAL PRESSURE TAP

FLOW REGULATOR, SELF-CONTAINED

3-WAY SOLENOID VALVE WITH RESET

PRESSURE-BALANCED DIAPHRAGM ACTUATED

AIR RELEASE VALVE

VALVE ACTION (SEE ABBREVIATIONS)

ROTARY PLUG VALVE

4-WAY SOLENOID VALVE

ROTARY ACTUATED

CONTROL VALVE WITH HAND ACTUATOR

DIAPHRAGM ACTUATED VALVE WITH POSITIONER (SHOWN ON SPLIT RANGE ONLY)

(E) CONTROL VALVES

FIGURE 6-1 (cont.)

Difference between Process and Engineering Flow Diagram Symbols

The difference is mainly one of detail; therefore, the individual examples shown in Chapter Four will not be repeated. The important point is that not a single line should be added unless it adds some extra clarification or additional information.

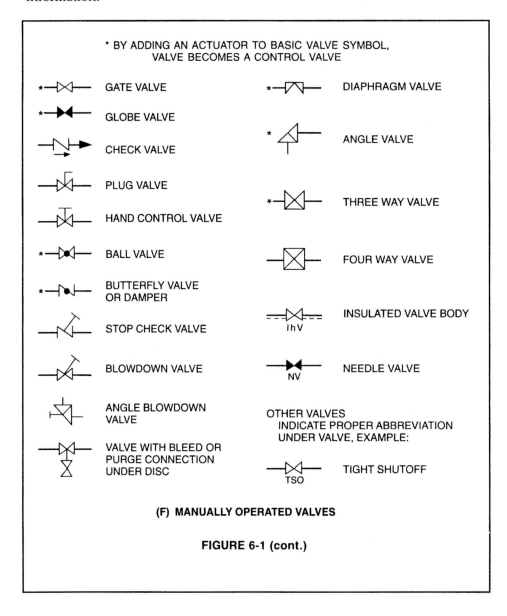

(F) MANUALLY OPERATED VALVES

FIGURE 6-1 (cont.)

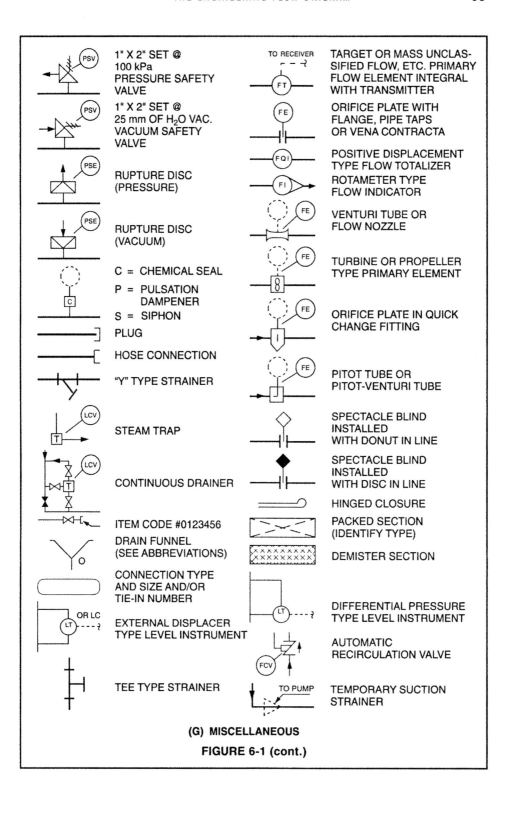

(G) MISCELLANEOUS

FIGURE 6-1 (cont.)

▨ WHAT IS AN ENGINEERING FLOW DIAGRAM?

An engineering flow diagram is a detailed graphic description of the process flow showing all the piping, the equipment, and much of the instrumentation associated with a given process. It is generated by the process engineer and sometimes is completed by the piping engineer. In any case, it is a multidisciplinary document since many disciplines will have input to the finished product.

The engineering flow diagram serves as the basis for process, piping, and structural design and reflects control systems design. A very important document, it is subject to formal reviews and approvals.

This diagram varies in style. It can be a single frame, which the author prefers, or it can be multiple frames, which some companies prefer. In any case, flow should proceed from left to right, and the drawing should be organized so that it consists of a process that can be grasped mentally.

There is always a tendency to put too much information on an engineering flow diagram. This applies not only to instrumentation details but also to information that appears on other documents. The danger in this is that a complete design must be depicted before all the details are complete. When information appears on more than one document, at revision time something always falls through the cracks.

▨ ENGINEERING FLOW DIAGRAM CHECKLIST

A checklist of what should appear on an engineering flow diagram follows. The list is not all-inclusive. Some of the items discussed in the checklist are shown in Figure 6-2, which treats each item separately since it is not possible to show a complete engineering flow diagram on a single 8-1/2 x 11 page.

Vessels

Figure 6-2 shows a typical vessel. Usually at the top of the flow diagram, above the vessel outline, appears a vessel title block with an underlined item number and an underlined title, the dimensions, and whether or not insulation is used and, if so, what type. Some companies add the vessel design pressure and temperature. The item number is repeated, underlined, inside the vessel outline.

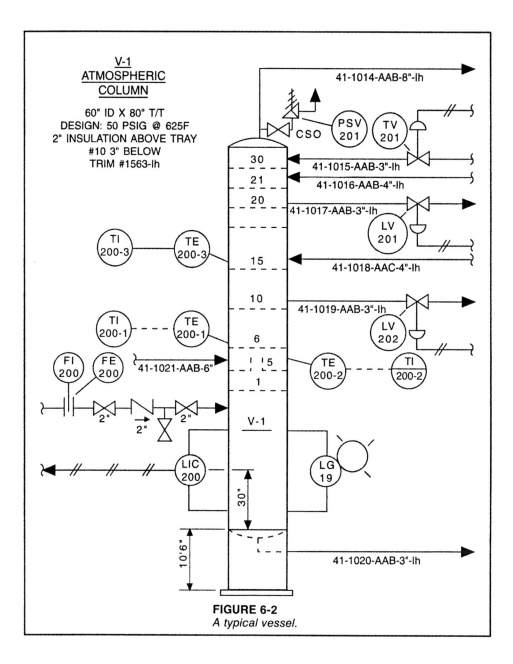

FIGURE 6-2
A typical vessel.

If the vessel contains trays, the top and bottom trays and any others necessary to locate connecting lines are shown. These lines may be sample lines or instrument connections. A convention for numbering trays must be established on the legend sheet.

The height and size of packing are shown. Catalyst beds, demisters, chimney trays, draw-offs, and similar important internals are usually shown.

It might sound trite, but it is important to check the mechanical vessel drawing against the flowsheet for consistency. The height of the tangent line of a vertical vessel is shown above the foundation. The height of the bottom of a horizontal vessel is shown above grade.

The height of the normal liquid level above the tangent line or above the bottom of a horizontal drum is shown. The range of controllers is not shown here, which would be premature, and it appears elsewhere.

Whether or not horizontal vessels are sloped is information that should be included.

Relief valves in refinery practice are usually shown on outlet vapor lines. In chemical plant practice they often are shown on the vessel, which obviates the necessity of performing inlet piping pressure drop calculations.

Heat Exchangers

Figure 6-3 is an example of how to depict a heat exchanger. Again, the item number and the title are underlined above the heat exchanger outline. Insulation, if any, is shown. Designation of design duty and design pressure and temperature are optional. The item number, underlined, is repeated next to the outline.

The correct type of exchanger is depicted, showing the number of shells or sections and the flow arrangement. The height above grade is usually indicated, and all vent lines are shown.

With utilities-type heat exchangers, the source and level of the utility are identified.

Pumps

Figure 6-4 shows how pumps are depicted on an EFD. The equipment title block should contain the underlined item number and title, insulation, and cooling water, flushing oil, or seal oil requirements. Design capacity and differential pressure are sometimes provided.

The type of pump and its driver should be shown; common spares are depicted. In this case the common spare is a steam turbine-driven pump. Minimum flow recirculation is shown where it is needed. Pulsation dampeners are shown on reciprocating pumps, and valved vents usually are shown on all pumps.

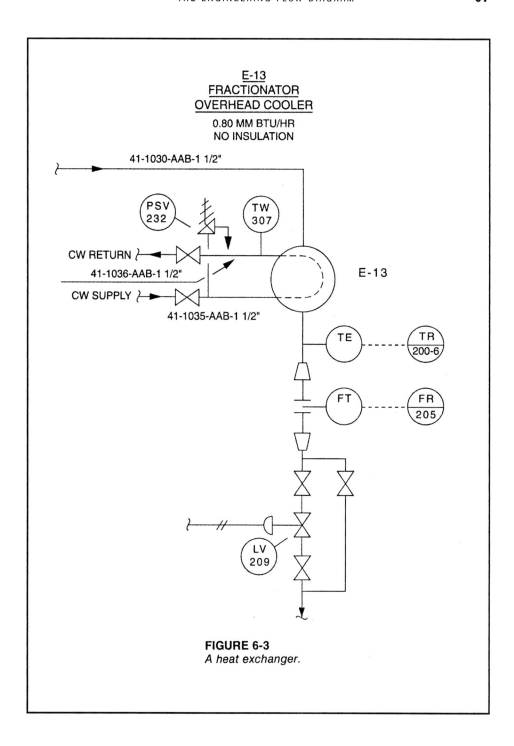

FIGURE 6-3
A heat exchanger.

Particular attention must be paid to pump controls. Automatically started spares must be depicted correctly. Automatic vent systems must be shown along with any necessary backpressure controllers.

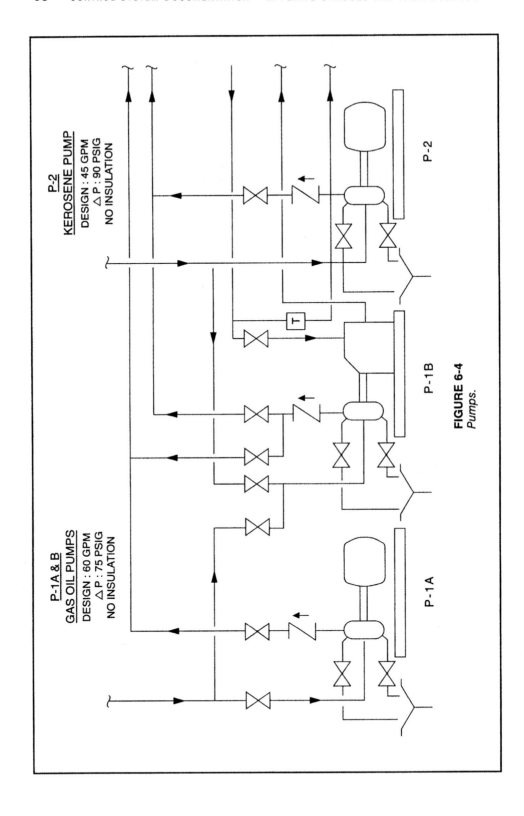

FIGURE 6-4
Pumps.

The sizes of the suction and discharge valves and the pump flange are depicted. Figure 6-4 is simply a bare sketch. Line numbers, pump outlet flange sizes, and other pertinent information would normally be added.

Compressors and Blowers

Figure 6-5 shows how typical compressors and blowers may be shown schematically. The type of compressor (centrifugal or reciprocating) and the number of stages should be shown.

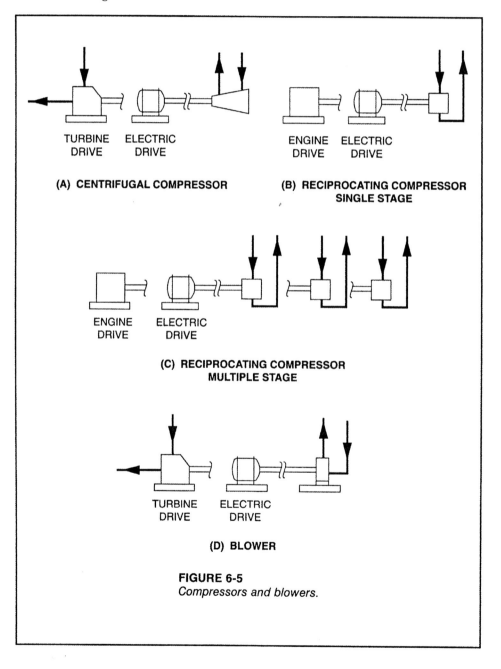

FIGURE 6-5
Compressors and blowers.

At the top of the drawing, as usual, above each compressor appear the item number and title, underlined, followed by design capacity, differential pressure, and brake horsepower.

The compressor specification sheet must be checked for consistency in the depiction of such things as nozzle sizes.

From a control point of view, the compressor is thought of as part of the process shown on the process flow diagram. However, on the engineering flow diagram, the auxiliary lube oil and seal oil may be depicted on a separate drawing. This is not a bad logical subdivision, since the first drawing concerns the relation of the compressor to the process and the second one concerns only the maintenance and operation of the compressor.

Cell Libraries

Cell libraries are an outgrowth of computer-aided design and drafting. Entire flow sheets, unit operations, equipment, and even instrument loops can be stored and recalled when needed. Software houses such as AutoCADD® and Intergraph® have developed standardized cell libraries that obviate the necessity of constructing all of the details of often-used figures. A cell may consist of a certain type of distillation column with all of its normal appurtenances. Instead of designing a specific column from scratch, the engineer might use the standard cell as a basis and simply change some of the details, thus saving time. Entire flow sheets, unit operations, equipment, and even instrument loops can be stored and recalled when needed. Large scale drawings can be constructed very rapidly. Computer-aided drafting is uniform and very professional looking.

There is one great danger in using large-scale cell libraries: they look so professional that errors can be made in assuming them to be correct for the real situation at hand. The authors have seen horrendous mistakes in design due to the fact that the so-called standard drawing did not, in fact, meet the needs of the real process, and insufficient time had been given to checking and modifying the standard drawing.

Instrumentation

Two great controversies exist in control systems work: how much instrumentation should be shown on an EFD, and what should be done about mechanical packages. Both controversies tend to disappear within a company when that company is consistent in its approach. They continue external to the company and will be examined separately.

▨ HOW MUCH TO SHOW?

An agreement must be reached regarding what instrumentation information is to be included on an engineering flow diagram. Since the document is a more or less complete shopping list of equipment, piping, and (to some degree) instrumentation, it could be argued that everything must be included. However, work schedules and drawing clutter have some influence on the decision. Not all instrumentation can be developed before the document is needed for other purposes; not all instrumentation needs to be shown on an engineering flow diagram. There is such a thing as information overload; the line must be drawn somewhere.

Obviously, space and locations must be reserved for piping and equipment, so all primary and final elements must be shown. The same applies to valves, sample points, PSVs, level glasses, TIs, PIs, flow elements, and so on. If the instrumentation is directly connected to the process, it should be shown.

Such things as valve sizes, set points, and failure positions need not be shown. They appear elsewhere, and it is unwise to place them where they possibly will not be revised at a later date. This type of information appears more logically on instrument data sheets.

Away from contact with the process is a controversial area. There are those who argue that only the basic loop should be shown—nothing more. On the other side are the larger companies that tend to perform their instrument design on the engineering flow sheet. Where is the line drawn?

The purpose of the engineering flow diagram is to depict the process in detail and to give some idea as to its control. Not all instrument details are shown—there are just too many. The basis already established is that all the instrumentation connected to the process and that information necessary to the operator are shown in detail but not the information that appears more readily elsewhere. Information that is necessary to the operator includes recording, indicating, controlling, alarming, and the availability of push buttons; it does not necessarily include square root extraction, for example.

Where does the information appear if it is not included on the engineering flow diagram? The answer is that it is on other documents: loop diagrams, logic diagrams, electrical control diagrams, ladder diagrams—whichever is most appropriate. Each company has to establish its own clearly delineated standards for documentation.

The authors' preference for engineering flow diagrams can be explained as follows. Basically, three major categories of instrumentation appear on the engineering flow diagram: analog-type controls, discrete controls, and the operator interface. Analog-type controls are those that deal with continuously controlled variables; discrete controls are those that are involved with logic. The operator interface involves everything the operator sees or touches in the supervision of the process. The EFD should show everything that the operator will see or touch: every indicator, recorder, controller, alarm, and push button that is connected with the process. The engineering flow diagram is the major source of the information about the process, so the operator must be able to see what will be available.

Discrete controls are probably the most complicated. Being complicated, they are difficult to depict, so they tend to be neglected. Many companies have attempted to invent a simplified logic to use on engineering flow diagrams, generally to no avail. The best approach to discrete logic is to show all the inputs and outputs to and from a rectangle that is identified as a logic block and then reference the drawing where the logic will be developed. This approach has the benefit of allowing development to proceed at a later time, yet giving the essential information for development of the engineering flow sheet—the inputs and outputs.

Analog-type controls are the most difficult to deal with because they seem to be the easiest to understand. The controversy concerning how much instrumentation should be included on an EFD really revolves around how much analog-type instrumentation is to be shown, if the reader accepts the authors' treatment of discrete logic. The roots of the controversy lie not so much in differences of opinion as in different company operating procedures. Since this type of difference cannot be resolved logically, a logical methodology will be presented, and the reader can be the judge.

The major part of the problem has been resolved by the statement that everything seen or touched by the operator and everything that touches the process must be depicted. What is meant by the word "depicted"? The basic symbols of ISA-5.1 should be shown, not PSV set points or vessel levels. Remember what happens to an engineering flow diagram: at some point in time it becomes cast in concrete. Usually this point arrives before the process instrumentation details are fully developed. Depicting details may seem like a good idea, but it may be extremely difficult to change them at a later time.

The same reasoning can be applied to thermowells. The use of a thermowell hinges on such things as speed of response. Indicating the use of a thermowell on a flow diagram is not really necessary since it is a detail that appears on a piping diagram and can be resolved at that time, when more information has been developed. Similarly, an I/P need not be shown. There is nothing wrong with showing an electrical signal going to a valve operator. That, in itself, conveys the information that an I/P must exist—and saves flow diagram room. Similarly, square root extractors and pneumatic or electronic switches need not be shown.

Where should these devices be shown? On the appropriate document: a loop diagram or equivalent.

WHAT TO DO ABOUT MECHANICAL PACKAGES

The easiest method to show mechanical packages is to draw a rectangle and reference a vendor's drawing. The most thankless task is to try to incorporate a mechanical package vendor's design into the overall process design. Different schedules, procedures, and methodology create too many conflicts for easy resolution.

The most difficult part is correctly portraying the interface between the vendor's package and the process design package. It is usually at the interface where things go wrong; they tend to fall through the cracks, as it were. Three wires come in and four go out, for example.

The authors' recommendation is to draw the rectangle with the reference, draw lines showing any interfaces to the package, and then carefully, very carefully, check the vendor's information to see that all assumptions are, and remain, valid.

SUMMARY

This chapter describes the engineering flow diagram (EFD) as a shopping list and a record of what has been decided elsewhere.

Since styles and symbols vary, the importance of the legend sheet is emphasized. Also, the reader is cautioned to build up from the process flow diagram symbols by adding only those lines that convey necessary information.

The use of cell libraries is discussed, and the reader is warned of their dangers.

Two controversial areas are discussed and the authors' preferences given.

Everything that interfaces with either the process or the operator must be shown. Everything else should be referenced to another document. Mechanical packages are best left to the mechanical package vendor; a block diagram showing the interface details is all that is required.

█ QUESTIONS

1. Why is the EFD described as 'a more or less complete shopping list'?
2. The authors spend a lot of time discussing legend sheets. Why?
3. What is the main difference between PFD and EFD symbols?
4. Why do the authors frequently caution against putting too much detail on drawings?
5. Why is a checklist a useful device?
6. What is the great danger involved in the use of extensive cell libraries? How would you overcome this danger?
7. What two areas do the authors regard as being 'controversial'? Why?
8. How is the above controversy usually resolved? How do legend sheets help?
9. Why is it important that every instrument that is to be connected to the process be shown on an EFD?

REFERENCE
1. ISA-5.1-1984(R1992), Instrumentation Symbols and Identification.

LOOP DIAGRAMS

▨ INTRODUCTION: NOT AN OPEN AND CLOSED CASE

Many hours have been spent discussing the merits of loop diagrams. Some have even denied their utility, arguing that the information contained therein could be found elsewhere—on engineering flow diagrams and on wiring diagrams.

Nevertheless, over the years loop diagrams have proven their worth. The thrust for their creation comes essentially from maintenance people who need a quick, convenient, and exact pictorial description of specifically what a loop contains.

Indeed, maintenance personnel usually want more detail on the loop diagram than design engineers think is necessary (or for which they have budgeted time). Unfortunately, this is a contractual problem that should be addressed at the beginning of a contract but rarely is.

▨ PURPOSE OF THE LOOP DIAGRAM

The purpose of the loop diagram is to show all the details of an instrument loop that the field instrument technician requires in order to check out and to troubleshoot the loop. In addition, the loop diagram is such a convenient maintenance document that many companies insist on putting calibration data on it. This practice, however convenient, breaks the golden rule—do not put a piece of information in more than one place. It leads to errors when drawings are revised. The instrument data sheet is specifically designed to carry this type of information and should be so used to avoid revision oversights.

Notice that, although a loop diagram for an electronic (4-20 mA dc) system looks like a wiring diagram, it really is not. An electrician wiring up a loop needs to know only where to connect the wires. This can be done with wire lists or point-to-point wiring diagrams. The loop diagram is intended for the instrument technician who needs to see the total interconnections of a single loop in an easily comprehended fashion. The loop diagram is also used for pneumatic loops for the same reasons.

The loop diagram is not used for installation, but it is used for installation checkout. Panel vendors also use it as an input to their detailed design, and it helps electrical designers develop cabling drawings and lists.

As far as the loop instruments are concerned, the loop diagram is a form of block diagram that shows the general locations of the instruments: panel, console, control room, rack room, and field. The instruments are identified by tag number, and the interconnecting wires and tubes are identified specifically, as are the terminals and termination points.

The loop diagram can be completed only after the choice of instruments has been made—usually after vendors' data has been received. This is where it differs from a conceptual design document. It is not a conceptual design document; it is a record of what has been designed.

Since a loop diagram shows only the principal instruments in the loop and not the process, some companies find it convenient to show a small flow diagram-style rendition of the same loop in one corner of the loop diagram. This also breaks the above golden rule, but it is a deviation that the authors can accept since it is very difficult to carry flow diagrams up a ladder on a troubleshooting mission. This is the only concession to be made, however, to bad practice. The habit of repeating what is contained on data sheets and in the instrument index is definitely bad practice.

■ WHAT SHOULD APPEAR ON THE LOOP DIAGRAM?

So, what should appear on a loop diagram? The title should be descriptive. Supplemental notes (brief) may be added to describe only that which is not evident from the symbols. Overrides, interlocks, cascaded set points, shutdown, and safety shutdown circuits may require brief notes.

Termination numbers should be provided; wiring and tubing identification by number and color is necessary. Junction boxes and bulkhead connections must be identified.

Wherever there is a change in circuit continuity (a termination of some sort), there must be some identifying symbol that will aid in checkout and troubleshooting. Locations are normally shown by dividing the drawing into sections, e.g., control room, rack room, field, etc.

Power sources and air and hydraulic supplies need to be specifically identified. The power level and circuit numbers are useful pieces of information.

WHAT NOT TO PUT ON THE LOOP DIAGRAM

The following should not appear on the loop diagram:
1. Other drawing references. These are already in the Instrument Index (This is not meant to exclude continuation references.)
2. Location information. This is on the location diagram.
3. Manufacturers' information. This is on the data sheets.
4. Calibration information. This is also on the data sheets.

There is always the tendency to feel that it is convenient to have the above information on the diagram. This can lead to disastrous consequences when the information is revised on one document and not on another.

SIZE AND FORMAT

The ideal size for the drawing is 11 by 17 inches which can be easily "Z" folded to 8-1/2 by 11 inches, 3-hole punched and inserted into a binder. Remember that this is the drawing that is likely to be carried up a ladder or studied by a technician while perched in some equally precarious position. What is convenient for an engineering office is not necessarily convenient for an instrument technician.

Usually, a horizontal format is more convenient due to the 11 by 17 inch diagram size. If the loop diagram is made on smaller paper, a vertical format may be applicable.

WHO DEVELOPS THE LOOP DIAGRAM?

The engineer usually initiates the loop diagram with a sketch. It is then passed to a designer for completion of the details. (As an aside, the designer will usually turn out a better looking product in shorter order.)

It is important that the engineer "compose the loop" himself or herself. Doing so gives the engineer a chance to look at all the items that have been selected and their locations. The designer then completes the work, also checking the work as it progresses.

▨ TYPICAL VERSUS INDIVIDUAL LOOP DIAGRAMS

Most large engineering companies prefer typical diagrams with specific details referenced in tabular form. Some even insist on putting many loops on one large sheet of paper because the engineering company is motivated by a concern for economy of its own time and effort, not necessarily that of the ultimate user.

Most users prefer individual loop diagrams, even if this should result in hundreds of loop sheets. This is because they are driven by concern for simplicity, exactness, and the need to carry only a few small pieces of paper when on a troubleshooting assignment.

Since loop diagrams are an operations-maintenance tool rather than an engineering tool, they are frequently given short shrift at the beginning of an engineering project. This fact often causes problems at the end of the engineering phase of a project when their worth is finally recognized. Perhaps a solution to this problem is to be found in the use of computer-aided drafting. It is now possible for an engineering company to create a set of loop diagrams with input data available at the time of the design and then to transfer the digitized information to the user company for further updating with operating-maintenance data.

▨ EXAMPLES OF LOOP DIAGRAMS

As always, a legend sheet specific to instrumentation should accompany a set of loop diagrams. The legend sheet serves as a quickly referenced memory jogger. It is also the place to define exceptions to the norm or special cases.

Again, the symbols should be related to symbols used in ISA standards (ISA-5.1 and ISA-5.4, for example) [Refs. 1 and 2]. Figure 7-1 is an example of a legend sheet for loop diagrams. It is not complete by any means and can be expanded upon with the specifics of each set of loop diagrams that it represents.

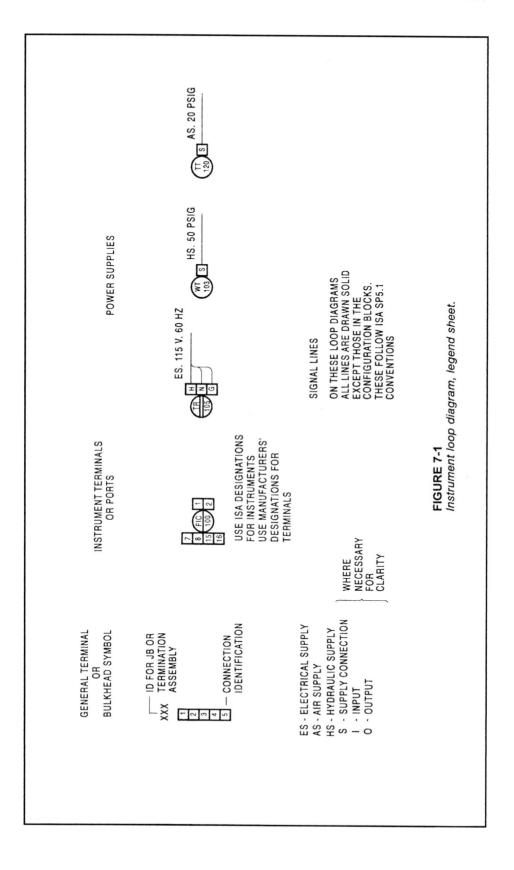

FIGURE 7-1

Instrument loop diagram, legend sheet.

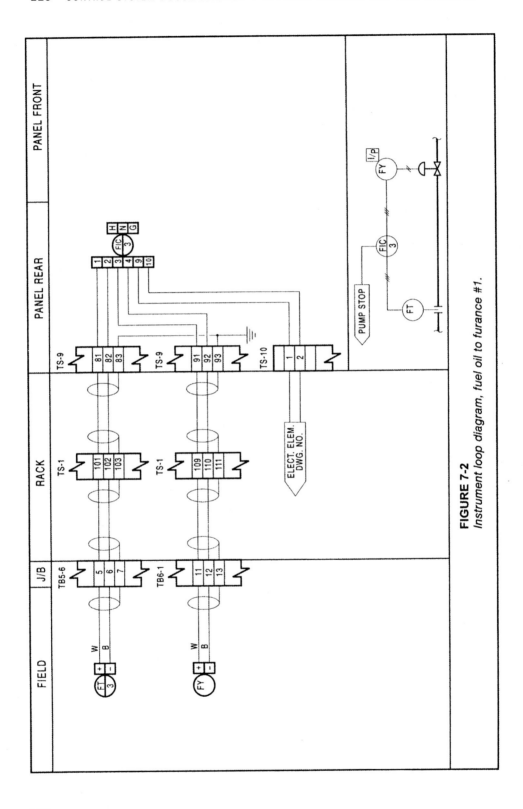

FIGURE 7-2
Instrument loop diagram, fuel oil to furance #1.

One important definition the legend sheet should contain is that of the line symbols. There are two schools of thought regarding line symbols. The first school adheres rigorously to ISA-5.1. The second prefers to use solid lines for all electrical symbols because most loop diagrams are electrical in nature, solid lines are simpler to draw than dashed lines, and the overall effect is more aesthetically pleasing.

The authors' preference is that, if the configuration block is drawn with standard ISA-5.1 line symbols, the lines in the loop diagram proper may be solid. No confusion can result when one has the configuration block to back up the legend sheet.

Figure 7-2 is an example of the layout of a typical loop diagram. The format is horizontal, 11 by 17 inches. The "boiler plate" is limited to a narrow strip at the bottom. Similarly, location descriptors are limited to a narrow strip at the top.

The loop diagram is broken into sections that correspond to locations, and the interface between adjacent sections corresponds to a physical interface. Interfaces are not arbitrary.

The flow diagram depiction (configuration block) is shown in the most convenient corner. And, since the primary and final elements are shown on the flow diagram depiction, it is not necessary to repeat them on the loop diagram proper. There will be exceptions to this economy of effort when it is necessary to identify a pneumatic bulkhead, for example, or when there is a choice of pneumatic connections on an electrical/pneumatic transducer.

Figure 7-2 is a good example of a typical electronic analog loop. It shows the essentials necessary for troubleshooting and no more. It stops either where the information is obvious (the field devices) or where the information requires a more complete depiction (the elementary diagram reference).

The headings are limited to a narrow band at the top of the sheet. The contract and revision data are limited to a slightly wider band at the bottom. The small configuration section could be in the left-hand corner just as easily as in the right-hand corner (or even in the middle if this space were available).

Figure 7-3 is an example of the use of "typicals." The loop configuration is common to a great many loops. The tag numbers, terminal strip numbers, and terminal numbers can be given in tabular format. "Typicals" work well with

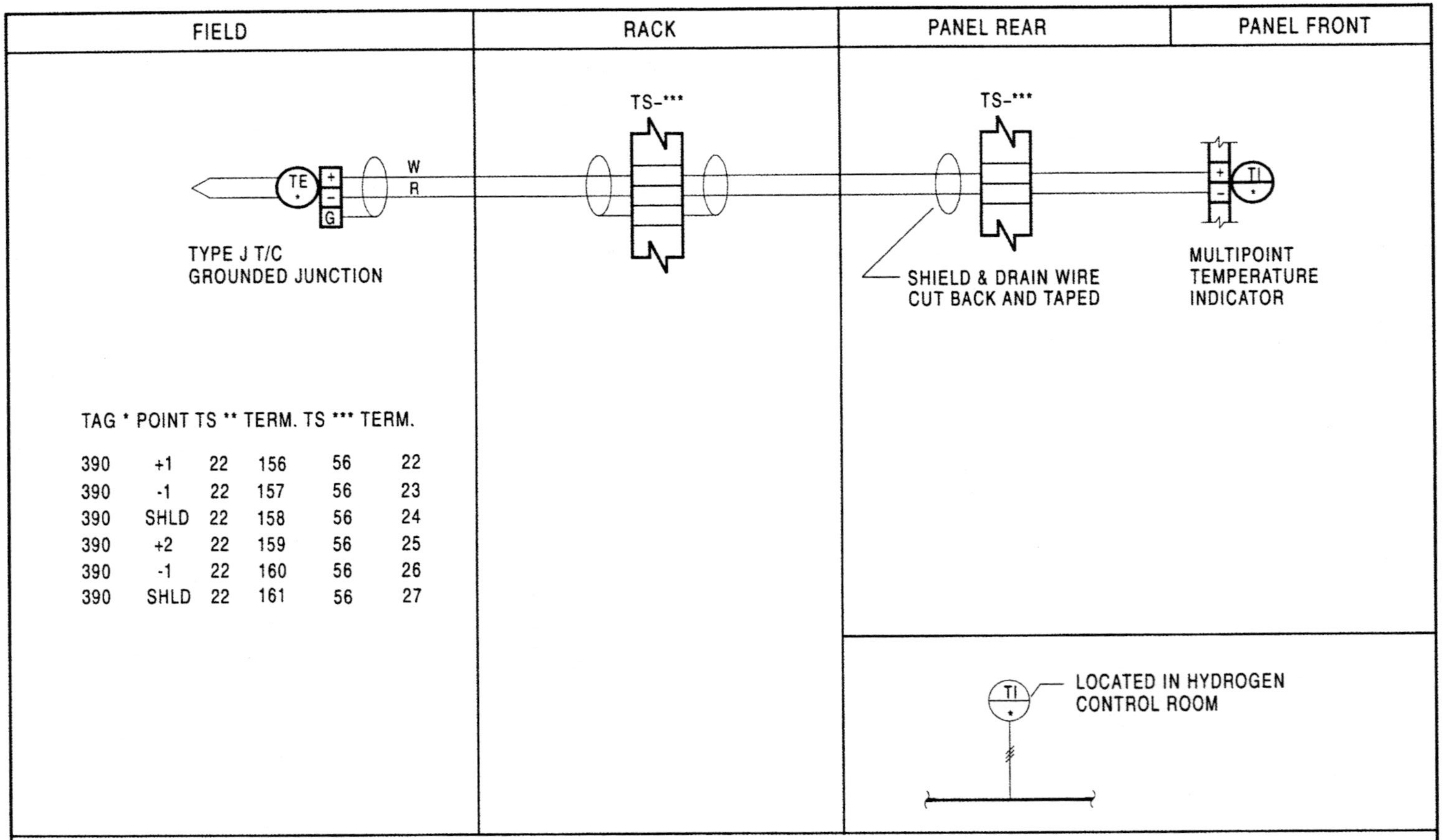

FIGURE 7-3
Typicals for multipoint temperature indicators.

repetitive loops of the type shown. However, their use is frequently overdone. Remember that simplicity of understanding is what the end user needs.

Figure 7-4 is an example of an alarm loop. A fair amount of controversy exists over whether or not loop diagrams should be made for non-analog loops. The ultimate user, the maintenance technician, usually prefers them.

The example shows how the more general symbols of ISA-5.1, shown in the configuration block, can be expanded with the aid of vendors' terminal numbers or letters placed in the terminal strips. Notice that the heading above the auxiliary panel has been changed to "FIELD ANNUNCIATOR PANEL." Notice also that an electrical symbol has been added to clarify the function of the pressure switch (normally open, held closed).

Figure 7-5 was chosen from real life to illustrate the difficulties that exist with color coding. It is easy for someone to arbitrarily establish that black is negative and white is positive (or vice versa). However, in real life a vendor whose favorite colors are blue and red may have supplied the panel.

When troubleshooting, the technician has to deal with someone else's follies. The problem of polarity is a common one that must be sorted out. The way to keep the polarity problem clear in one's mind when dealing with analog DC current loops is to look for the loop power supply—in this case, the speed transmitter, ST-902. Terminal 12 is identified as the positive terminal, and Terminal 13 is the negative terminal.

The power supply is a source of current; every other instrument in the loop is a sink. The first instrument connected to either wire from the source must be connected to a terminal of the same polarity as the source. Polarity is then alternated around the current loop.

For instance, in Figure 7-5, ST-902 Terminal 13 is identified (from vendor's data) as being negative. The first instrument connected to it is S1-902 B. The connection is to the negative terminal (negative to negative). After this first instrument, polarity is alternated. The positive terminal of S1-902 B is connected to the negative terminal of S1-902 A. The positive terminal of S1-902 A is connected to the negative terminal of SSL-902 (Terminal 2 from vendor data). The positive terminal of SSL-902 (Terminal 1) is connected to the positive terminal of ST-902, the original source.

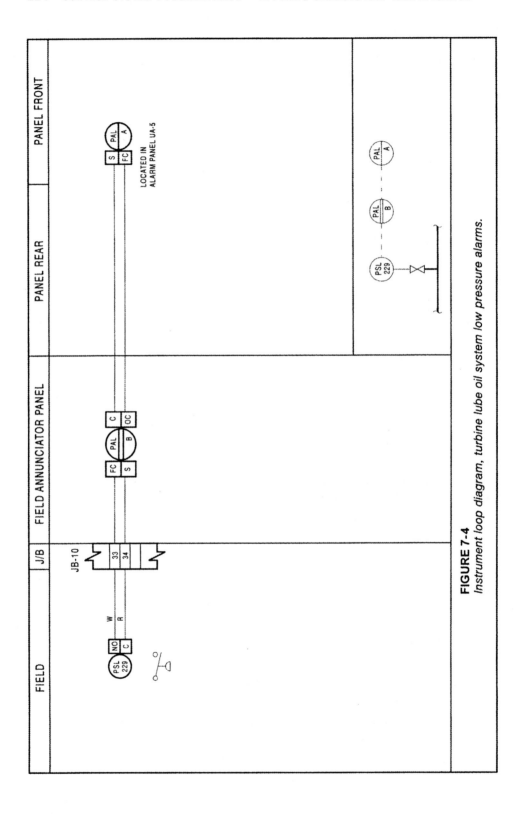

FIGURE 7-4
Instrument loop diagram, turbine lube oil system low pressure alarms.

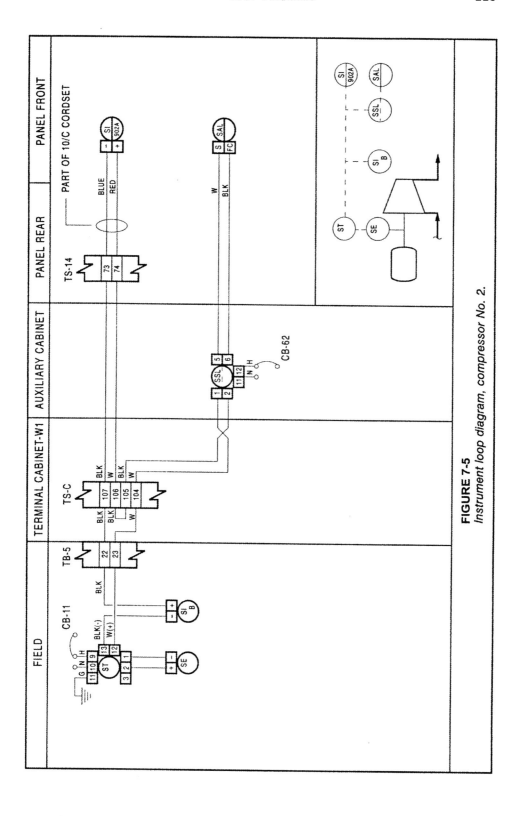

FIGURE 7-5
Instrument loop diagram, compressor No. 2.

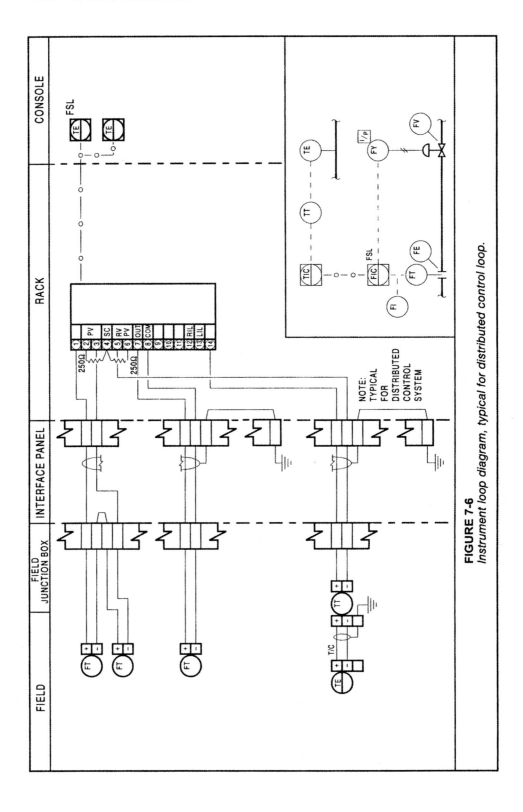

FIGURE 7-6
Instrument loop diagram, typical for distributed control loop.

The above description is correct since SSL-902 is the first instrument connected to the source while proceeding in the opposite direction around the loop. This time the connection is positive to positive.

The point being made is that with a knowledge of analog current loops and some vendor data, no matter how confusing the color code may be, it is still possible to troubleshoot the loop.

Notice that this example has again changed the heading of the sections (TERMINAL CABINET-W1, AUXILIARY CABINET). Notice also that circuit breaker symbols and information have been added.

One additional comment on this example: The authors have followed the convention of showing the loop number only once, since it is common to all instruments in the loop. It is also correct, however, to include the loop number in every bubble.

Figure 7-6 is a typical loop diagram for a distributed control system. It shows how to handle the case in which the actual wiring differs somewhat from the engineering flow diagram depiction shown in the configuration block.

The rack-mounted controller would be given an identifying tag number. Actually, if it were involved only with the two loops shown, it could carry both tag numbers.

It is tempting to stop the loop diagram at the inputs to the rack-mounted controller, since this is usually all that is needed for troubleshooting. However, the remainder of the loop drawing is necessary for completeness.

Notice also that the rack-mounted controller is shown as a block. This is a common practice. In fact, the terminal strip could have had two adjacent instrument bubbles inscribed FC-99 and TC-201 for instance, and the data highway could have joined both of them.

SUMMARY

This chapter clarifies the confusion surrounding the justification for the production of loop diagrams, that justification being their utility as aids to troubleshooting and checkout.

Unfortunately, troubleshooting and checkout are the direct concern of only a few technicians who usually not only insist on loop diagrams, but usually insist on having more information on them than the original design engineers are willing to spend time developing.

Those who have not been concerned with troubleshooting and checkout find it easy to say that the information can be found elsewhere. This is true, but the convenience of the loop diagram and its importance in getting a process started back up after a shutdown far outweigh any perceived redundancy. Design engineers can now put on the drawing the information that is readily available to them during the design phase. Maintenance personnel can add calibration information to the same document. However, the authors argue strongly against putting information that is likely to be revised on more than one document.

The most convenient size for the loop diagram is 11 by 17 inches, and a horizontal format is the most common. Each drawing should contain only a single loop. An exception to this may be simple loops where the different tag numbers can be easily tabulated, but this practice is easily overdone.

A legend sheet must accompany any set of drawings, and loop diagrams are no exception. It is not necessary to invent new symbols since most necessary symbols can be taken directly from ISA-5.1 or ISA-5.4. Block symbols and electrical symbols also are found on many loop diagrams.

Some advice is given on how to deal with polarity in a current loop. Wire color codes can be confusing in a series loop.

Finally, six examples are given. There is a certain sameness about loop diagrams and the examples may look simple. However, a lot of thought must go into the preparation of something that finally appears to be simple. Only your local maintenance technician will really appreciate the effort that goes into their preparation.

▨ QUESTIONS

1. Who benefits most from a loop diagram?
2. Why are there so many different opinions about their utility?
3. What is the primary purpose of a loop diagram? When is it most frequently used? By whom?

4. List those things you think should be mandatory on a loop diagram.

5. List those things that sometimes appear on a loop diagram, but would be better placed elsewhere. Where?

6. What is the ideal size and format of a loop diagram? Why?

7. To what extent do you agree with the use of 'typicals'?

8. Why do the authors mention the legend sheet so often?

9. Sketch a number of series connected instruments in a loop diagram format and show the correct polarity.

10. Why does the instrument technician wish to see manufacturer's information and calibration information on the Loop Diagram?

11. Some of the new instrument databases provide the ability to automatically generate loop diagrams from information entered into the database. What effect could this have on the amount of information included on the Loop diagram?

REFERENCES

1. ISA-5.1-1984(R1992), Instrument Symbols and Identification.

2. ISA-5.4-1991, Instrument Loop Diagram.

8

LOGIC DIAGRAMS

▓ INTRODUCTION: AND, OR, NOT, NEVER, MAYBE

In control systems engineering, the word "logic" is often used in terms of relay "logic" or programmable controller "logic." The term is usually associated with the concept "binary," which means, "possessing one of two possible states such as on-off, high-low, greater-lesser, present-absent." The word "logic" refers to a system that obeys a fixed set of rules and always presents the same set of outputs for the same set of inputs, although these responses may be modified by some internal condition such as the state of an output from a timer.

Relay Logic, Binary Logic, and Programs

Early relay logic was used for simple interlocking in electrical control circuitry. If a motor draws too much current, it must be tripped. If an electrical heater gets too hot, it must be turned off. If a conveyor belt is running off to one side, it must be stopped. For a given set of inputs, a decision must be made and an action taken.

Combinatorial or Sequential Logic

Often, an attempt is made to distinguish binary, event-driven, or instantaneous logic from sequential logic. This has more to do with the difficulties associated with depicting the latter than any real differences. In fact, it is probably wrong to try to make a distinction, since both forms exist in most control schemes.

Sequential logic has been less satisfactorily handled in the past than has been combinatorial logic. It is usually depicted in a way that demands too much technical knowledge on the part of the nontechnical reader who must, nevertheless, pass judgment on the document. Fortunately, a much simpler methodology has been developed that should make the exchange of concepts much easier. IEC Publication 60848 (published 2002) [Ref. 1] describes this methodology under the title, "GRAFCET Specification Language for Sequential Function Charts." These function charts will be discussed in greater detail later in the chapter.

In the past, few would have recognized the words "binary logic" or "program," yet binary logic programs were exactly what was being created with ladder diagrams and wiring schematics. In fact, anyone who has tried to find the way through a complex ladder diagram must have wished for an easier way. There is no easy way, but binary logic diagrams are used in an attempt to render the job easier, to make it less dependent on knowledge of specific hardware, and to make it more functional in orientation.

PLC Logic

Programmable logic controllers (PLCs) have now replaced complex relay systems. They consume less space, are less expensive where large numbers of functions are involved, and are more readily modified than are hard-wired relay systems. Programmable logic controllers are frequently programmed by emulating relay ladder diagrams since these diagrams are readily understood by many people. The problem still remains that ladder diagrams tend to be too hardware-oriented and require knowledge of electrical circuitry that sometimes gets in the way of the creative process. Binary logic diagramming is an attempt to reduce, to the simplest representation, the complex logic that exists between the inputs to a system and its outputs.

One great advantage of binary logic diagramming over ladder diagramming is the ease with which binary logic can be combined with a depiction of the process being controlled, which gives a clearer understanding of the connection between the two. Even though a programmable logic controller might eventually be programmed using ladder diagram symbols, it is still easier to work with and understand the basic scheme when it is first sketched using binary logic.

▨ TWO PHASES—CONCEPTUALIZATION AND EXECUTION

There is a subtle but very important distinction between the two major phases that must be considered in achieving a workable control scheme that involves binary logic. The first phase is common to all hardware; the second is much more dependent upon the specific hardware used. The first phase answers the question: What needs to be done to control a certain process? The second phase answers the question: Given what needs to be done, how does one do it?

By breaking up the design process into these two phases, much can be accomplished. The problem can be clearly defined without the constraint of the need for detailed knowledge of available hardware. It can be discussed among people who may be knowledgeable about the problem but who may have different degrees of knowledge regarding the hardware (or software) available for its solution. When the design process is resolved into its component parts in this more or less abstract fashion, the problem and its solution can be conceptualized, a hardware choice can be made, and the solution can be executed rather efficiently.

The first phase is conceptualization. Since the objective is to conceive of control schemes that involve a process, logic to control that process, and the operator interface that permits the operator to intervene from time to time, it makes sense to include all these elements in a conceptual sketch or drawing. The second phase, execution, involves execution details or instructions to a programmable logic controller. This phase requires knowledge of only immediate inputs, not the process conditions that generated them. It makes sense, in this phase, to eliminate much of the extraneous detail that relates to the process or to operator interface requirements.

Document Types

In going from concept to execution, it can be seen that at least two types of documents are required. The execution document is often the only one that sees the formal light of day. The conceptual document exists either as an engineering sketch or an attempt is made to combine it with an engineering flow sheet. For complex logic, the latter is completely unsatisfactory. Much confusion could be avoided if the conceptual document were a stand-alone sketch or drawing.

In fact, more than two types of documents are involved in going from concept to execution. As usual, the conceptualizing process starts right at the beginning, with the process flow diagram. About this time, a general, brief, narrative description (usually in print form) outlines the process, what is to be accomplished, and the operator interface requirements. When the engineering flow diagram is developed, at least the inputs and outputs to the logic system should be fixed. Once the inputs and outputs are fixed, the conceptual logic document can be made. When the conceptual logic document has met with general approval, the execution documents can be begun.

The choice of the plural in the expression "execution documents" is deliberate. It is possible to go directly from the conceptual logic document to a ladder diagram as the final execution document for relay or programmable controller logic. However, on large systems, it is usually preferable to have an intermediate document that can be understood by those who do not necessarily understand the details of ladder diagram logic. This document can also be used for checkout purposes since it shows all internal logic and symbolizes all inputs and outputs without any extraneous process or operator interface details.

The final execution document is usually some form of ladder diagram. It is a standard electrical ladder diagram if relay logic is involved and a programmable logic controller ladder diagram if a PLC is used. In the latter case, it may even be generated by the PLC if the programmer chooses to go directly from the logic diagram to the keyboard. In this event, it still serves as a record of the actual logic in place.

The authors have a rather strong opinion about the role that the engineering flow diagram (mechanical flow diagram, P&ID, etc.) should play in the depiction of logic. It should show all the input devices and output devices to and from the logic system and that they are connected to it by the use of the generalized logic diamond. It should make no attempt to show how the logic functions. To do so, even when the logic has been designed, results in either too much clutter or over simplification. When the logic has not yet been designed or ascertained, as is often the case with third-party engineered packages such as those associated with turbines and compressors, it frequently results in totally incorrect depictions that must be changed later.

Conceptual Logic Documents

The conceptual logic drawing attempts to answer the question: How do we get there from here? As has been stated, the engineering flow diagram is an inadequate design tool for logic purposes. In addition, ladder diagrams are too specialized for conceptualization purposes. Therefore, the conceptual diagram's greatest utility is as a tool that permits the logic designer to reason through and present process logic without too much concern for the specifics of the ultimate hardware to be used to execute the logic.

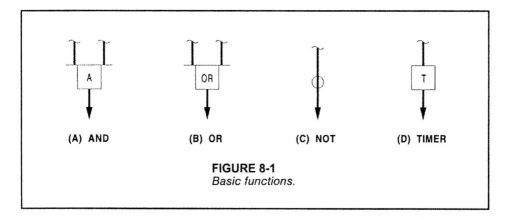

(A) AND **(B) OR** **(C) NOT** **(D) TIMER**

FIGURE 8-1
Basic functions.

There are three basic divisions in the conceptual logic drawing. One section shows the process being controlled without going into details that have no impact on the controllability of that process. A second section shows the logic. Another section shows the operator interface, since nothing is entirely automatic.

The basic logic symbols are extremely useful tools (Figure 8-1). They can be used to develop and to depict extremely complex logic in an understandable fashion. Figure 8-1(A) represents an AND gate, both of whose inputs must be present before there can be an output. Figure 8-1(B) is an OR gate, which can have an output any time any input is present. Figure 8-1(C) is a NOT gate, or an invertor, which changes the sign of the input. Figure 8-1(D) is a simplified, general symbol for any time function.

▨ LOGIC EXAMPLES

In the following sections, we will discuss several logic examples including the holding circuit, field functions and a batch chemical reactor.

The Holding Circuit

One of the most common logic circuits is the holding circuit used for electrical motors (Figure 8-2). The figure shows the division of the flowsheet into a panel area, a logic area, and a field area (other areas, such as a rack area, could be added if necessary). The START push button sends a signal to the OR gate, which passes any signal it receives. The signal goes to the AND gate, which will produce an output only when all its inputs are present. Since the STOP push button is not being depressed, the NOT gate inverts the zero signal to a positive signal, satisfying the AND gate, and an output is produced. As well as

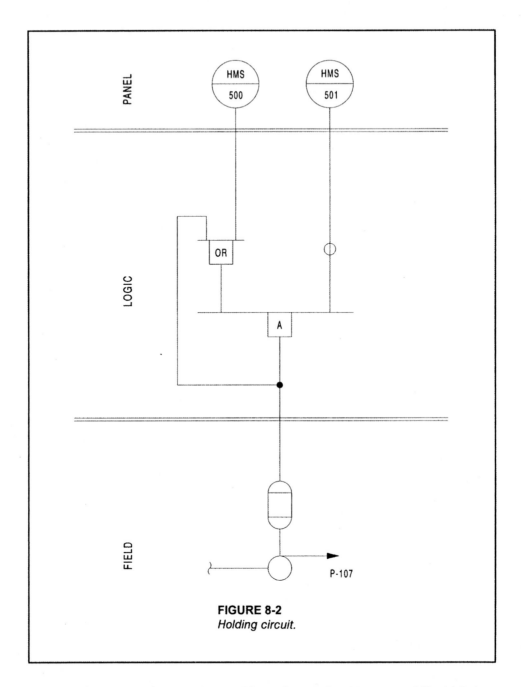

FIGURE 8-2
Holding circuit.

going to the motor, the output signal branches to the OR gate and "holds" the logic, even when the START push button is no longer depressed. When the STOP push button is depressed, the NOT gate inverts the positive signal so that the AND gate is no longer satisfied, and the holding circuit "drops out."

Note that it took many words to describe a simple system that can be readily grasped once the intended meanings of a few symbols are known. Note, also, that only the basic functions are depicted in the figure. Process logic, not equipment protection, is of concern. Therefore, overload relay and other interlocking is not shown (although it could be if protection were the primary concern). In addition, note that it appears as if the motor receives its power from the logic. This is obviously not so, but the depiction is simple and does not detract from an understanding of the circuit.

Field Functions

The next example (Figure 8-3) is slightly more complex. It shows how the basic holding circuit may be expanded when field inputs and parallel outputs must be considered.

The process involves evacuation of equipment (by a liquid-sealed vacuum pump) that could be under a greater pressure than the pump case rating. The vacuum pump has two levels of protection: the primary protection is the PSV; the secondary is the low pressure switch whose function is to avoid unnecessary operation of the PSV. The block valve holding circuit has a permissive input from the low pressure switch, after a time delay, to avoid action due to spurious signals. The vacuum pump holding circuit has a parallel output to the seal water solenoid valve.

Notice that positive logic is used. The PSL puts out a positive signal (a logic 1) when the line pressure is below one pound per square inch gage (1 psig). The STOP push buttons have positive outputs only when depressed. Their normal state is a logic 0. No thought need be given to the state of the contacts (normally open, normally closed) since this would cause the designer's mind to wander from the problem at hand, which is to conceptualize the process control logic. Since the block valve fails closed (arrow on the stem), a positive signal opens it. A positive signal starts the vacuum pump motor and opens the fail-closed solenoid valve.

The example shows how pilot lights may be depicted as one means of operator interface; push buttons are the other, in this case. Obviously, the example could show more protective interlocking, and a more automatic control scheme could be used.

Batch Chemical Reactor

The next example is deliberately more complicated. It is based on a hypothetical batch reactor example used by Zoss [Ref. 2] many years ago to illustrate older, relay-based logic. Zoss immediately had to instruct his readers on the

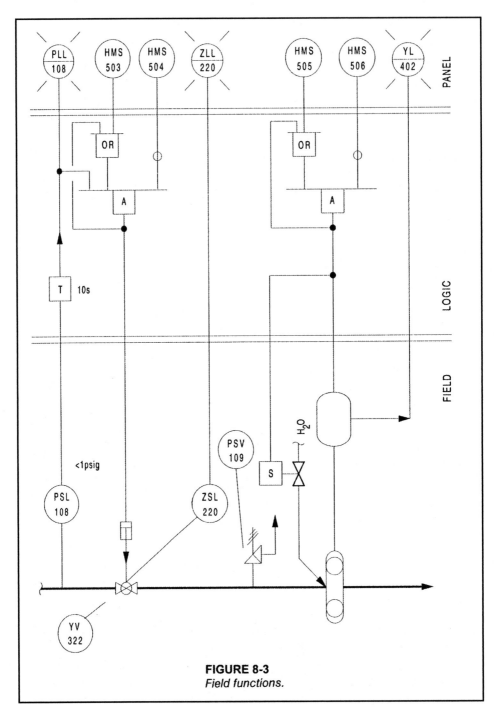

FIGURE 8-3
Field functions.

peculiar characteristics of the hardware involved in order that they might have
some understanding of the symbols used to depict the logic. Since one of the
aims of this book is not to let hardware get in the way of the conceptualizing
process or of understanding, the same system will be approached from a more
fundamental level. The logic will be hardware-independent. Only a basic

understanding of field and panel devices will be assumed. As the system is more complicated, a narrative description is necessary. See Figures 8-4, 8-5, and 8-6 for what follows.

Narrative Description

Process
1. A jacketed stirred tank reactor must have X m^3 of ingredient A added; then it must be filled to a volume defined by LSH 2 with ingredient B.
2. Once the measured volume is established, the agitator can be started and the heating sequence begun.
3. The heating sequence must follow the temperature profile of Figure 8-6.
4. The sequence involves two upward temperature ramps at different rates, two holding periods, and a downward ramp.
5. At the end of the downward ramp, the agitator must be stopped and the kettle drained.

Operator Interface
The operator interface is mainly by push buttons, selector switches, pilot lights, and horns. The operator is permitted manual control of each step within certain constraints and he or she may also initiate a completely automatic sequence.

Logic

Step	Description
1.	Fill with X m^3 of A, but check first that the kettle is empty and the outlet and B ingredient valves are closed.
2.	Add ingredient B to level of LSH 2, but check first that the outlet and A ingredient valves are closed.
3.	Start the agitator and go to the procedure (temperature ramp) phase.
4.	Follow the required temperature profile.
5.	When the temperature profile has been traversed, stop the agitator and empty the reactor, making sure that the fill valves are closed. During the emptying phase keep cold water circulating through the jacket.

Logic Description

Once a general narrative description has been established, it would be normal to proceed directly to the logic sketch. What follows is not necessary to the design process. It is a description intended for those unaccustomed to logic

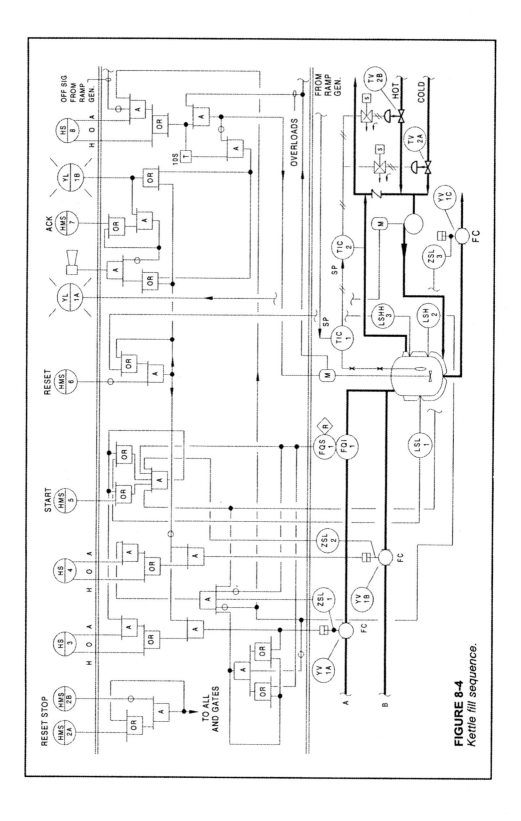

FIGURE 8-4
Kettle fill sequence.

diagramming. The authors have chosen to repeat parts of the process schematic in two sketches for convenience of representation in a text. In practice, a single, full-sized drawing would probably be used.

The description starts at the left of Figure 8-4. A standard holding circuit is used as an emergency STOP/RESET permit to all AND gates (HMS 2A/B). To allow the system to function at all, the RESET button must be depressed. Pushing the STOP push button disables all AND gates and causes the system to go to its fail-safe mode. Lines could be drawn to the AND gates, but the simplification does not harm understanding.

A constraint has been added to the fill sequence: an excessively high level must prevent further filling. This is accomplished by a signal from LSHH 3, which triggers another holding circuit that must be reset by HMS 6 when the high level condition has been corrected. An output from this holding circuit closes or prevents opening of the fill valves whether they are in the manual or the automatic mode. The output also causes a horn to be sounded and a pilot light to be lit. The horn may be silenced by the ACKNOWLEDGE button, HMS 7, through its holding circuit, but the light will be lit as long as the reset push button, HMS 6, is not depressed.

The fill valves, YV lA and YV lB, may be opened manually by putting HAND-OFF-AUTO selector HS 3 in the HAND position. The only constraint is that LSHH 3 must not have been actuated. These selectors will normally be in the AUTO position, as will be the agitator selector HS 8.

In the automatic mode, the operator need only press the START push button, HMS 5. The conditions for this command to be followed are dictated by the inputs to the AND gate below HMS 5. It can be seen that YV lC must be closed (ZSL 3 actuated), YV lB also must be closed (ZSL 2 actuated), the manual reset button on flow counter switch QS 1 must be depressed, and the reactor must be empty (LSL 1 actuated). If these conditions are met, an output results, and two of the conditions are immediately bypassed: the actuation of the START button and the requirement that the reactor be empty.

The output of the AND gate goes to the other AND gate under the AUTO position of HS 3. Since the selector is in AUTO, valve YV lA will open (no high-high level). FQI 1 will begin to meter the required amount of feed material into the reactor. When FQS 1 trips, a permit is removed from the start circuit's AND gate. The gate is disabled, which disables the first gate in the YV lA circuit and causes the valve to close.

The next step in the automatic sequence is the opening of valve YV lB. The requirements for its opening may be seen from the inputs to the AND gate feeding the gate under the AUTO position of HS 4. This gate requires that LSH 2 not be actuated, that ZSL 1 confirm closure of YV lA, that ZSL 3 prove closure of YV lC, and that FQS 1 be counted out (signal has gone to zero and has been inverted). Since all these conditions are also present at time zero, it is necessary to add a condition that confirms execution of the previous step. The last permit comes from a gate that is actuated when YV lA is commanded to open, the flowmeter is operating, and the level is not high. A holding circuit holds around the first two conditions and supplies the correct logic to the previous gate. The logic causes closure of YV lA to be the trigger that opens YV lB.

LSH 2 supplies the signal that closes YV lB and resets the above-mentioned logic, thus ending the fill cycle.

The next step in the sequence is to start the agitator. In the automatic mode this occurs when the signal from LSH 2 enables the AND gate below the AUTO position of selector HS 8. Since no OFF signal is being received from the ramp generator, all permits are present and the gate is enabled. The output passes through the OR gate and does two things: it initiates a ten second timing sequence and starts the motor, provided it is not in an overload state. Should the motor not start within the ten-second period, the timer output will enable the other AND gate and annunciate the failure condition via the horn and pilot light previously described.

The agitator will be stopped when the ramp generator's OFF signal becomes active. This will be discussed in the next phase.

The procedural sequence may be followed with Figure 8-5. HS 9 initiates this phase when in the HAND position and supplies a permit to the first AND gate when in AUTO. A second input comes from the agitator RUN signal. The other input to the AND gate comes from LSH 2, and it is bypassed by a holding circuit in order to avoid false stoppages when the agitator starts and the liquid surface becomes choppy.

Since it is not permitted to heat up the reactor without agitation, the agitator RUN signal also supplies a permit to the HAND position AND gate.

Outputs from either of the two AND gates pass to the OR gate and result in the solenoids, which held the heating and cooling valves in their failure positions,

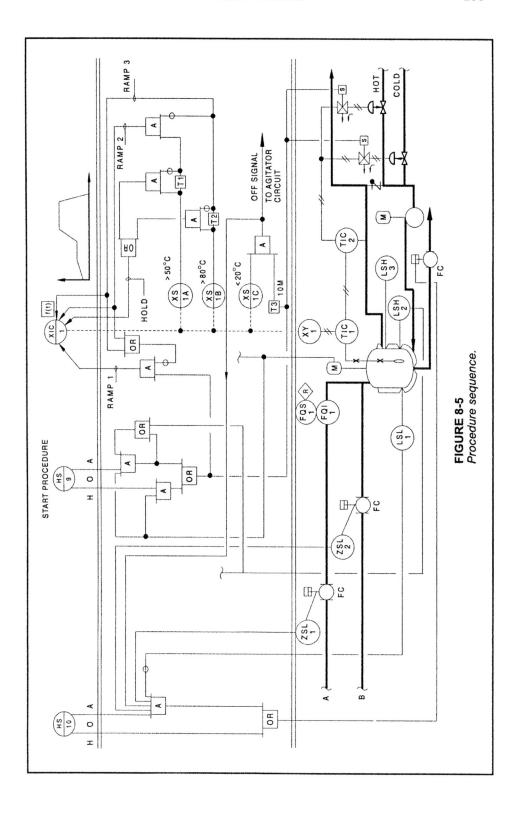

FIGURE 8-5
Procedure sequence.

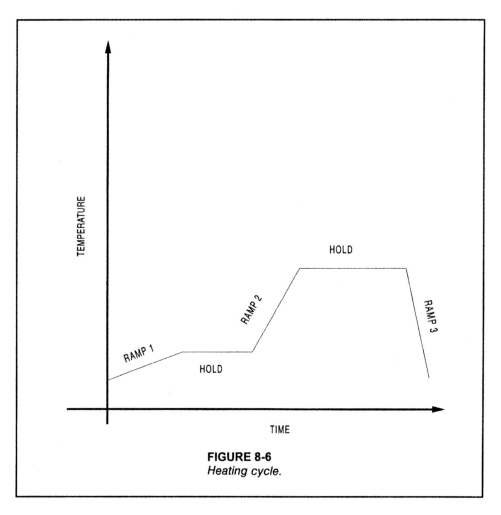

FIGURE 8-6
Heating cycle.

being energized. The split-ranged heating and cooling valves will now follow the output of TIC 2 (for the initiated, anti-reset windup will have been used). At the same time ramp generator XIC 1 will receive a signal that causes it to follow its first temperature ramp.

As an aside, the only knowledge of the ramp generator needed is that such a device exists, that it has binary inputs to govern its ramp rates and their directions and the hold functions, that it has an electronic analog output, and that it is panel-mounted. The ramp generation function could be achieved in other ways, but for the purposes of this exercise the above is satisfactory.

The binary signal marked RAMP 1 causes the ramp generator's output to increase at the rate dictated by the first part of the temperature profile of Figure 8-6. When the first temperature hold point is reached, the switch XS 1A will initiate the first hold period through timer T1. This is conveniently done with the use of an AND gate that is enabled only when the timer is initiated but not yet timed out. When the timer times out, the HOLD is removed by the NOT gate and the RAMP 2 command is given.

The RAMP 2 command causes a similar sequence of events, although the rate is different. The second plateau is reached when XS 1B triggers the HOLD command and governs its length through T2. When T2 times out, the RAMP 3 command causes the negative portion of the temperature profile to be followed down to the value set by XS 1C.

The purpose of the T3 timer is to inhibit the OFF signal from XS 1C, which occurs at the beginning of each cycle. It must shut off the agitator only during the downward ramp. When the agitator is shut off, the permit signals to the START PROCEDURE gates are removed, the solenoids are deenergized so that cooling fluid is circulated in the jacket, and a HOLD command is sent to the ramp generator via the inverted RAMP 1 signal.

The AND-NOT-OR combinations present on each RAMP command are intended to ensure the presence of only one of these signals at a time. They also inhibit these signals during the HOLD periods.

The next phase is emptying the kettle. It can be seen from the logic beneath HS 10 that the reactor may be emptied completely when HS 10 is in the HAND position. When in AUTO, emptying depends upon the inlet valves being closed, the OFF signal being sent to the agitator at the end of the PROCEDURE phase, and LSL 1 not being actuated. The agitator OFF signal from the ramp generator logic initiates the emptying phase, and the signal from LSL 1 (when the low level in the reactor is reached) ends it. All logic conditions are now reset for a restart on operator command.

Pictures Worth Thousands of Words

The foregoing logic description should be proof positive that a picture is often worth more than a thousand words. It took several thousand words to describe two relatively simple sketches. Once certain symbolic conventions are agreed upon, the same amount of information may be conveyed in a noncontradictory fashion by the use of very simple geometric figures. This simplicity and conciseness is both the beauty and the strength of binary logic symbols.

Although in what has preceded the value of logic symbols as a tool of the conceptualization process has been stressed, its usefulness does not stop there.

136 CONTROL SYSTEM DOCUMENTATION – APPLYING SYMBOLS AND IDENTIFICATION

Once conventions are established, the logic is very objective and noncontradictory. Unlike word descriptions, logic sketches are not open to interpretation; what you see is what you get. Therefore, more than one person can contribute to logic diagrams. They can be checked, discussed, revised, approved, and used for checkout purposes. They make an excellent instruction tool.

In checking, checkout, and instruction, a systematic method of tracing through the complexity is required. A good method of following the logic is to use a felt highlighter pen to trace lines from a convenient starting point to a logical end point.

FUNCTION CHARTS FOR CONTROL SYSTEMS

IEC's Technical Committee 3, Subcommittee 3B: Documentation has published a method (IEC Publication 60848-2002) of describing the function and behavior of control systems that lends itself to both conceptual design and description of sequential logic. The method can also be combined directly with the usual combinatory logic to form a powerful design tool.

French Norme NF C03-190 TR1 [Ref. 3] formed the basis for IEC 60848 and hence. GRAFCET is the French name the given to the method.

Function charts are made up of steps, directed links, and transitions (Figure 8-7). The step describes a (sometimes momentary) steady state of a sequential process. The directed link shows the direction of flow of the logic. The transition is used to depict the conditional change between steady states.

Actions, statuses, or commands from the logic are associated with steps. Conditions or commands to the logic are associated with transitions (Figure 8-8). Commands or actions are qualified by the letter symbols S, D, L, and P, which stand for STORED, DELAYED, LIMITED (in time), and PULSED (briefer than LIMITED). The letters may be formed into combinations (Figure 8-9). Commands or actions may be conditional—letter C (Figure 8-10).

Transitional conditions may be represented by textual statements, Boolean expressions, or graphic symbols (Figure 8-11).

One powerful capability of these function charts is that they can represent parallel logic paths, either exclusive sequence selection (Figure 8-12) or inclusive sequence selection (Figure 8-13). In Figure 8-12 the exclusivity is denoted by

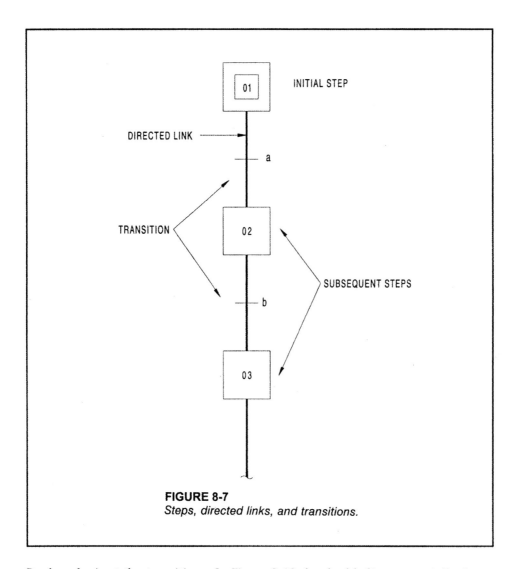

FIGURE 8-7
Steps, directed links, and transitions.

Boolean logic at the transitions. In Figure 8-13 the double lines, especially the lower ones, depict simultaneity. In this case transition c is not enabled until both steps 09 and 10 are active at the same time. Then, and only then, may the transition be cleared.

For more detailed descriptions, see Reference 1.

EXECUTION DOCUMENTS

The bias of a conceptual logic diagram is toward solution of the problem of how to control a process; that of an execution logic diagram is toward putting the solution into effect. Conceptual logic has just been discussed; execution logic will now be considered.

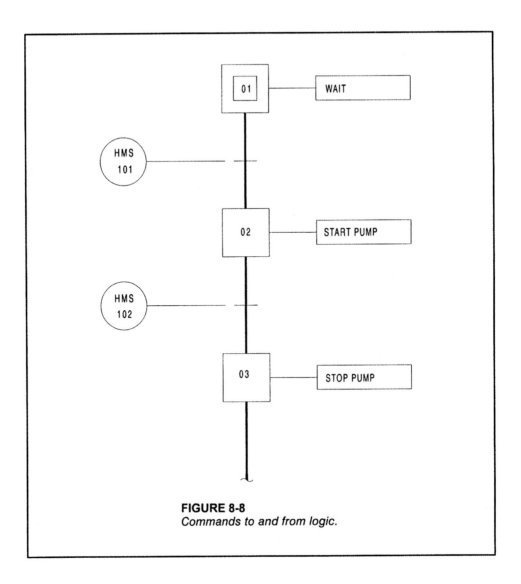

FIGURE 8-8
Commands to and from logic.

An execution logic document is any document intended as a tool to have instructions carried out, either by other designers and engineers or by programmers. The document is at least once removed from conceptual design. The original thinking has largely been done, and the emphasis is on conveying information to someone who is more concerned with executing the design or with having it executed.

The authors put ISA-5.2, Binary Logic Diagrams for Process Operations, in the category of execution documents since it concerns itself only with inputs, outputs, and the intervening logic. It is at least once removed from the process in that no process schematic is utilized.

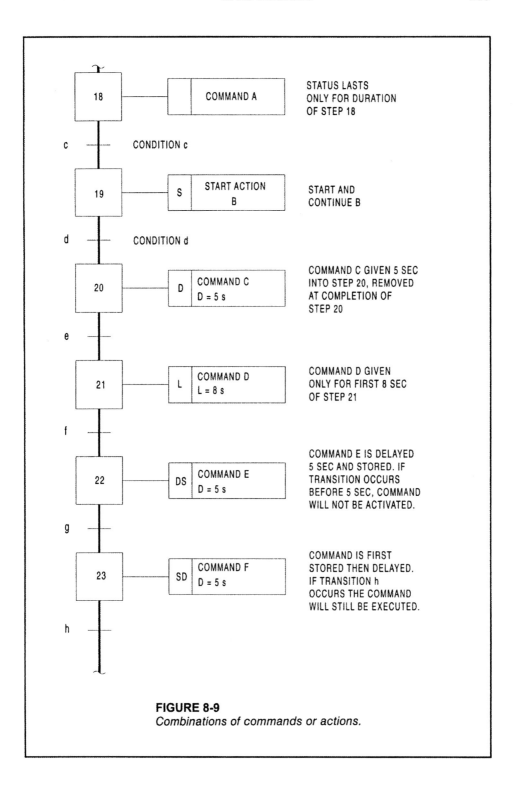

FIGURE 8-9
Combinations of commands or actions.

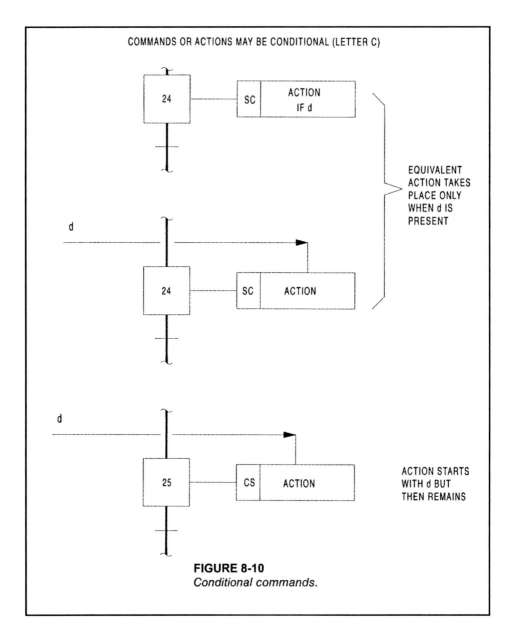

FIGURE 8-10
Conditional commands.

Other standards such as ANSI/IEEE STD. 91-1984, Graphic Symbols for Logic Diagrams (Two-State Devices) [Ref. 4] and the NEMA standard ICS 1, Industrial Control and Systems: General Requirement, [Ref. 5], are even more removed from the process. The ANSI/ IEEE standard gets down to the printed circuit board level, and the NEMA standard is not too far behind.

Since this book is process applications-oriented, it assumes that the degree of detail present in ISA-5.2 is more than adequate for applications engineers and designers. Applications-oriented people need to understand the process and

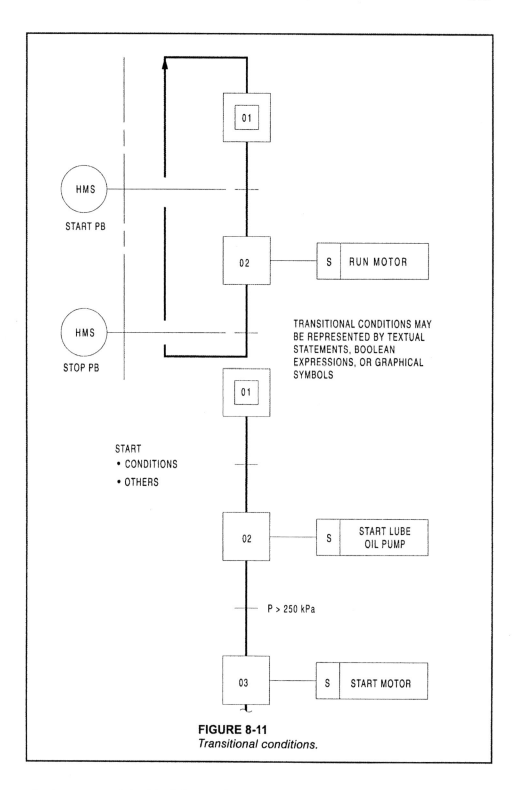

FIGURE 8-11
Transitional conditions.

the functions of the black boxes they apply to the problem of process control; they do not have to get inside the black boxes.

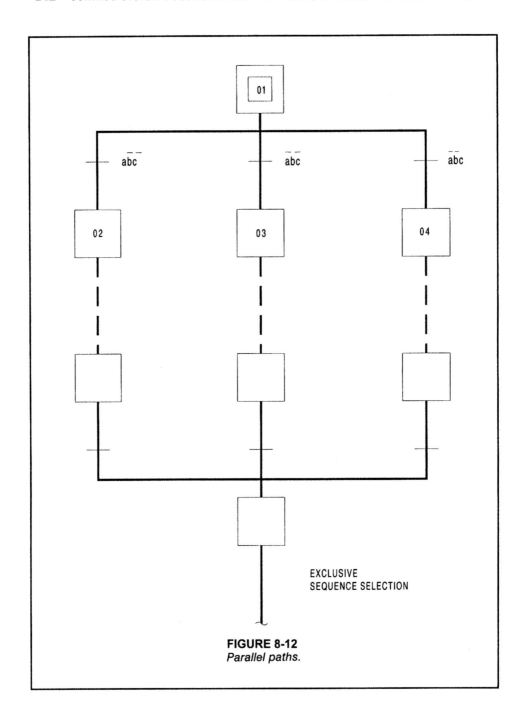

FIGURE 8-12
Parallel paths.

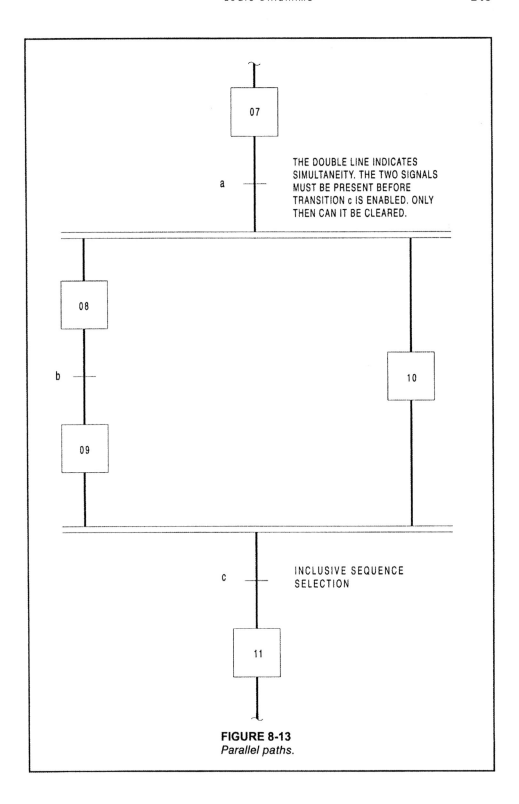

FIGURE 8-13
Parallel paths.

ISA-5.2, Binary Logic Diagrams for Process Operations

This standard's field of application is found in its statement of purpose, which is to provide a method of logic diagramming of binary interlock and sequencing systems for the start-up, operation, alarm, and shutdown of equipment and processes in the chemical, petrochemical, metal refining, and numerous other industries. The standard is intended to facilitate understanding of the operation of binary systems and to improve communications among technical, management, design, operating, and maintenance personnel concerned with systems.

Given the classification of conceptual versus execution documentation, management and operating personnel probably would find greater utility in the former than in the latter. The connection with the process is much more explicit.

Differences between Conceptual and Execution Document Symbolism

The first difference is orientation on the drawing. Conceptual diagramming lends itself to a vertical orientation, as processes are usually seen to run horizontally and the signal lines are best shown perpendicular to the process. Execution diagramming lends itself to a horizontal orientation, almost like a ladder diagram, possibly because there is generally more narrative and possibly because the logic is followed sequentially without too much concern for the process.

Another difference is that conceptual logic is best drawn on full-size drafting paper, while execution logic is often drawn on 8-1/2 X 11 inch paper. In the first case, the format helps in visualizing the overall picture; in the second case, convenience of handling is probably more important, and the overall picture is secondary to the logic itself.

A third difference is that the logic gates in the conceptual logic are easier to draw. Since this logic is usually drawn in the form of freehand sketches, it is important that a minimum of lines, symbols, and letters be used.

The Logic Diagram

Before a logic diagram can be developed, a flow diagram must exist. Figure 8-14 is such a flow diagram. There would normally also be a brief, point-by-point, narrative description of the designer's intent. Then the logic diagram would follow. Figure 8-15 is the logic diagram associated with the flow diagram of Figure 8-14.

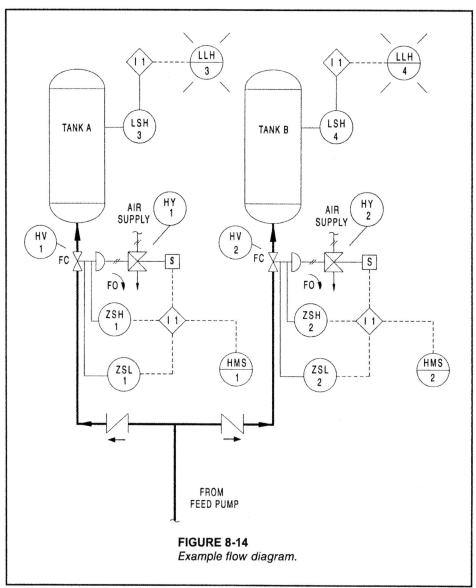

FIGURE 8-14
Example flow diagram.

The diagram shows many of the symbols of binary logic for process operations. The input and output function symbols are the instrument bubbles and flags of ISA-5.l. Input and output statements are interposed between the bubbles or flags, and the logic and continuation arrows lead the logic from one drawing to another. Logic flows from left to right. Arrows are used only where necessary for better understanding of signal flow.

Here are some of the salient points regarding logic presentation as depicted in Figure 8-15:

1. The drawings are easier to follow if all inputs are shown on the left and all outputs on the right. Logic functions are shown in the middle.

2. Even though the position switches, ZSH and ZSL, are actuated by the valves, HV-1 and HV-2, the switches are an input to the logic and the valves are an output. They may be connected physically, but as far as the logic is concerned the switches are drawn on the left as inputs, and the valves are drawn on the right, as outputs.

3. The NOT gates should be a little smaller in relation to the instrument or device bubbles. There is no necessity to stop the logic line on either side of the gate. In practice, the line is drawn and the circle is drawn over it.

4. The START and STOP push buttons are given the same tag number; however, they are different functions and should be differentiated. If it is desired to maintain the same basic number because they may be in the same physical case, a letter or number suffix could be used. Even this is not absolutely necessary, however, since the switch could be tagged with different numbers separated by a slash.

5. Sometimes it is tempting to maintain the loop concept (HS 1, HV 1, ZSH 1). This is always an unfortunate choice since it is rarely possible in practice in other than trivial cases. In addition, it is misleading since ISA-5.1 calls for a new loop number with each new measured or initiating variable. Only if the H-variable loop and the Z-variable loop were the very first two loops to use these letters could there be correspondence.

6. In connection with the above, most systems of moderate complexity do not have one-to-one relationships between input and output functions. If they had, they would be manual systems. It is best to face complexity at the outset and give the logic system the designation YIC (or YC if it is blind). The system is, after all, an event controller. Similar output elements would be given alpha or numeric suffixes.

7. One last suggestion is that, although the logic may be quite abstract, the connections to it must be quite concrete. Figure 8-14 shows only a single physical output to a three-way solenoid valve. The connection to the logic must reflect this. There is no CLOSE VALVE output function. To close the valve, the OPEN VALVE signal is removed. Two outputs are needed only if there are two solenoids.

Since this is an execution document, it is preferable to use the identification of the connected devices (i.e., the solenoid valves, not the line valves) and to observe the failure modes of the connected devices.

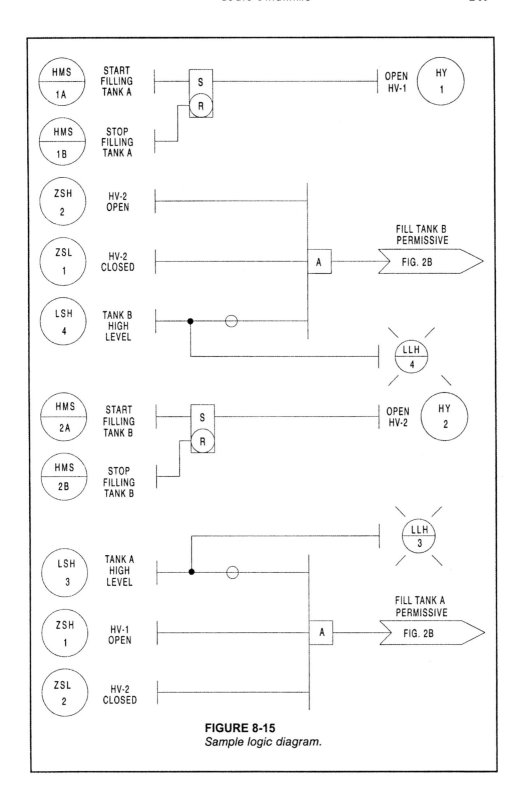

FIGURE 8-15
Sample logic diagram.

It is wise to observe the safe failure modes. The authors feel very uncomfortable with fail-open fill valves and with high logic levels used to "deenergize" solenoids. The first is unlikely and the second is confusing.

The Logic Elements

Figure 8-16 gives symbols for and examples of the basic logic functions. Here are some more pointers on good practice:

1. Do not use words when symbols and identifiers are available. When words must be used, they should be used in a concise fashion. Even if a tag number is not available, the identifier portion can be used to avoid a narrative description.

2. Function 1, Input. If the logic lines lead directly to an output labeled Conveyor Start, then the words could be omitted, especially if HS is replaced by HMS (hand-momentary-switch). If not, then the words Start Conveyor (one above the other) save horizontal space and, together with HMS, would convey all the needed information without redundancy.

3. Function 2, Output. When there is a choice between, words and symbols, choose symbols or a combination of symbols with a briefer statement of output. There is a much greater impact on pattern recognition when this alternative is chosen.

   The first-letter (H) should be used only if there is a direct connection to a hand switch. If not, it is wise to treat the logic as a system and use Y for event or K for time, depending on whether the logic is largely event-driven or time-driven. In these cases, all outputs would carry the same loop number and different suffixes.

4. Function 3, AND. The words on the inputs and output simply help tie the symbol to the definition. Logic is the art of noncontradictory identification. Which tank, valve, or pump is being discussed?

   The two inputs carry more information in a more specific fashion if bubbles with the function identifiers LSH and ZSH are used. If it were felt necessary to identify the tank and the valve, the equipment and valve identifiers (i.e., T-3, HV-7) could be used, if they exist. If not, more specific words such as Slurry Tank and Slurry Pump Suction Valve would have to be used.

   The output is also nonspecific. If it were known that a specific relay was actuated to start the pump, then a bubble with the relay tag number could be used (i.e., YY 6).

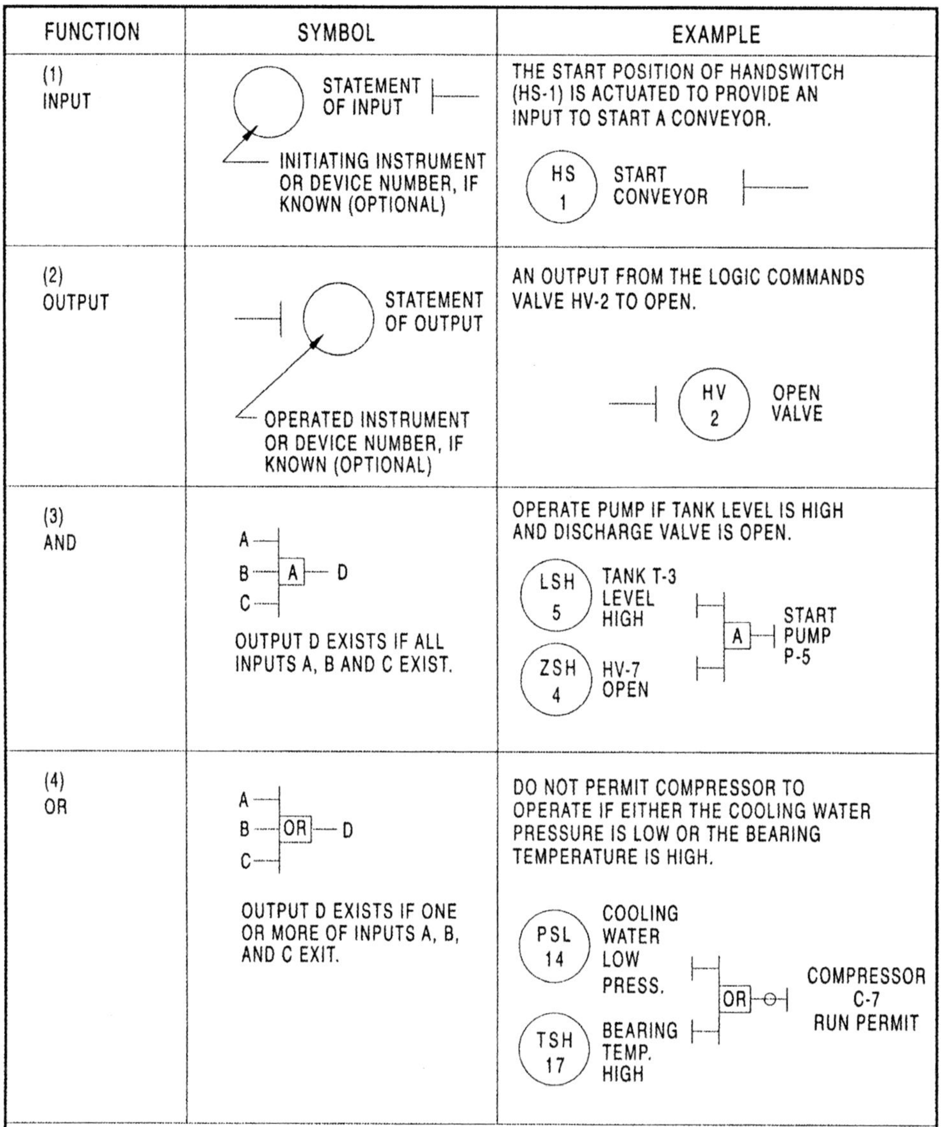

FUNCTION	SYMBOL	EXAMPLE
(1) INPUT	STATEMENT OF INPUT ⊢— — INITIATING INSTRUMENT OR DEVICE NUMBER, IF KNOWN (OPTIONAL)	THE START POSITION OF HANDSWITCH (HS-1) IS ACTUATED TO PROVIDE AN INPUT TO START A CONVEYOR. (HS 1) START CONVEYOR ⊢—
(2) OUTPUT	—⊣ STATEMENT OF OUTPUT — OPERATED INSTRUMENT OR DEVICE NUMBER, IF KNOWN (OPTIONAL)	AN OUTPUT FROM THE LOGIC COMMANDS VALVE HV-2 TO OPEN. —⊣ (HV 2) OPEN VALVE
(3) AND	A— B—[A]— D C— OUTPUT D EXISTS IF ALL INPUTS A, B AND C EXIST.	OPERATE PUMP IF TANK LEVEL IS HIGH AND DISCHARGE VALVE IS OPEN. (LSH 5) TANK T-3 LEVEL HIGH ⊢— (ZSH 4) HV-7 OPEN ⊢— [A]—⊣ START PUMP P-5
(4) OR	A— B—[OR]— D C— OUTPUT D EXISTS IF ONE OR MORE OF INPUTS A, B, AND C EXIT.	DO NOT PERMIT COMPRESSOR TO OPERATE IF EITHER THE COOLING WATER PRESSURE IS LOW OR THE BEARING TEMPERATURE IS HIGH. (PSL 14) COOLING WATER LOW PRESS. ⊢— (TSH 17) BEARING TEMP. HIGH ⊢— [OR]—○⊣ COMPRESSOR C-7 RUN PERMIT

FIGURE 8-16
ISA logic symbols.

5. Function 4, OR. Most people feel very uncomfortable if a positive output has to occur for a machine to stop. In the absence of a positive command, the concept of fail-safe requires that the machine stop. This output is inverted using a NOT gate and the words Compressor Run Permit are used in place of Stop Compressor.

6. Function 5, Qualified OR. The qualified OR is not frequently needed but when it is it allows simplified depiction of otherwise complicated logic. The same suggestions that were made above regarding identifying

FUNCTION	SYMBOL	EXAMPLE
(5) QUALIFIED OR	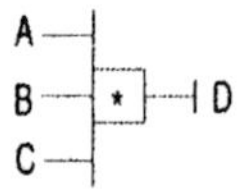 A ─┐ B ─┤ * ├─┤ D C ─┘ * INTERNAL DETAILS REPRESENT NUMERICAL QUANTITIES (SEE BELOW) LOGIC OUTPUT D EXISTS IF AND ONLY IF A SPECIFIED NUMBER OF LOGIC INPUTS A, B, AND C EXIST. MATHEMATICAL SYMBOLS, INCLUDING THE FOLLOWING, SHALL BE USED, AS APPROPRIATE, IN SPECIFYING THE NUMBER: a. = EQUAL TO b. ≠ NOT EQUAL TO c. < LESS THAN d. > GREATER THAN e. ≮ NOT LESS THAN f. ≯ NOT GREATER THAN g. ≤ LESS THAN OR EQUAL TO (EQUIVALENT TO f) h. ≥ GREATER THAN OR EQUAL TO (EQUIVALENT TO e)	a) OPERATE MIXER IF TWO, AND ONLY TWO, BINS ARE IN SERVICE.  RED BIN IN SERVICE ├────┐ BLUE BIN IN SERVICE ├──── ┤=2├ OPERATE WHITE BIN IN SERVICE ├──── MIXER YELLOW BIN IN SERVICE ├────┘ b) STOP REACTION IF AT LEAST TWO SAFETY DEVICES CALL FOR STOP.  DEVICE #1 ACTUATED ├──── DEVICE #2 ACTUATED ├──── DEVICE #3 ACTUATED ├──── ┤≮2├ STOP DEVICE #4 ACTUATED ├──── REACTION DEVICE #5 ACTUATED ├──── c) OPERATE MATERIALS FEEDER IF AT LEAST ONE AND NO MORE THAN TWO MILLS ARE IN SERVICE. MILL #1 IN SERVICE ├────┐ MILL #2 IN SERVICE ├──── ┤≥1 / ≯2├ OPERATE FEEDER MILL #3 IN SERVICE 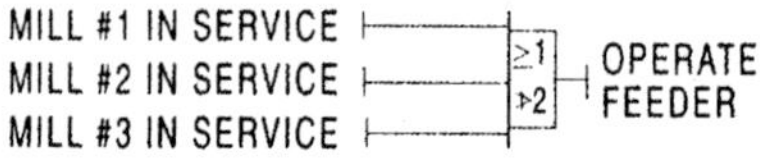 ├────┘

FIGURE 8-16 (cont.)
ISA logic symbols.

input and output devices apply. Similarly, the same concern for a fail-safe mode must be felt. If an exothermic reaction has the possibility of running away, it is best to show the logic as positive in order to keep the reaction going. Failure of the logic should stop the reaction.

7. Function 6, NOT, shows the equivalence between an AND gate with NOTs on its inputs and an OR gate with a single NOT on its output. The truth table demonstrates the equivalence. (As mentioned above, the authors prefer a smaller NOT circle on the logic line, without a break. Sometimes a tangent circle option is used. This is not necessary. It is better to have consistency, and the practice seems to cause a slight loss of clarity.)

8. Function 7, MEMORY. The example is worth discussing from two aspects; the first has already been referred to but bears repetition.

FUNCTION	SYMBOL	EXAMPLE
(6) NOT	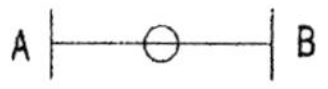 A ─○─ B OUTPUT B EXISTS ONLY WHEN INPUT A DOES NOT EXIST.	CLOSE VALVE HV-7 WHEN TANK T-3 LEVEL IS NOT HIGH AND PUMP P-4 IS NOT RUNNING.

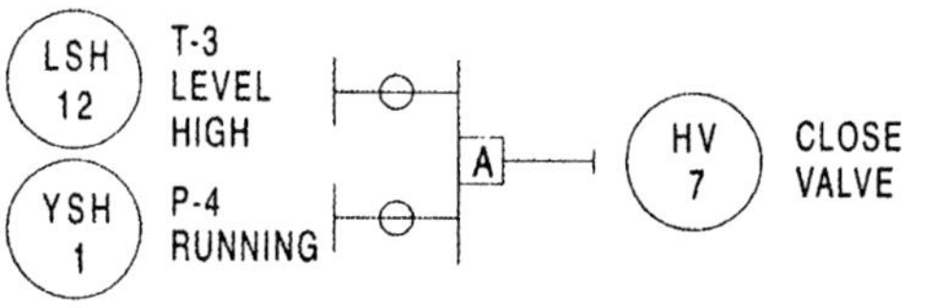

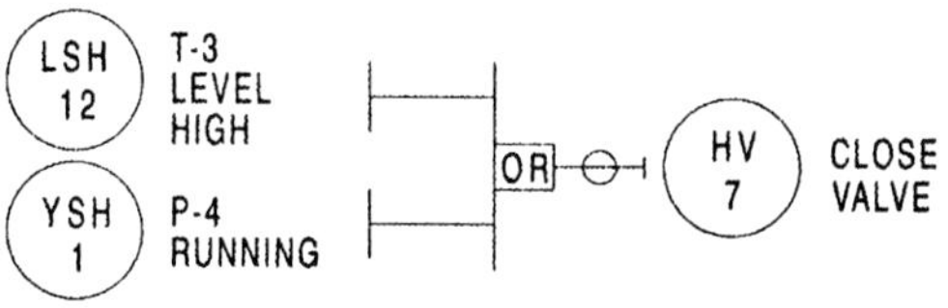

TRUTH TABLE TO SHOW EQUIVALENCE

INPUTS		OUTPUT	
LSH 12	YSH 1	HV 7	
		CASE-1	CASE-2
1	1	0	0
1	0	0	0
0	1	0	0
0	0	1	1

NOTE: A LOGIC "1" IMPLIES THE EXISTENCE OF AN INPUT OR OUTPUT SIGNAL, AND A LOGIC "0" IS THE ABSENCE OF A SIGNAL.

FIGURE 8-16 (cont.)
ISA logic symbols.

The combination of ISA-5.1 symbols and identification with specific equipment identifiers permits a concise depiction. The second aspect is application to a real process situation; it exemplifies the principle that one should not become so abstract that one loses sight of reality. Consideration of failure modes of the tank vent and of the pump start permit require the vent to fail open and the permit to fail off.

The loss-of-power supply options (L—lost, M—maintained, N—not significant) can be misleading, and they are really meaningless in the light of present-day technology, which permits permanent memory even with no power supply. The reason that they are misleading stems from the fact that, when deciding failure modes, the total picture must be considered,

FUNCTION	SYMBOL	EXAMPLE
(7) MEMORY (FLIP-FLOP)	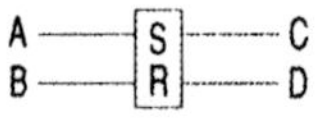 A ——[S]—— C B ——[R]—— D INPUT-OVERRIDE OPTIONS: IF BOTH INPUTS EXIST AT THE SAME TIME AND IT IS DESIRED TO HAVE ONE OVERRIDE THE OTHER, THEN A CIRCLE SHOULD BE PLACED AROUND THE MEMORY STATE (S OR R) THAT IS TO GOVERN, I.E. 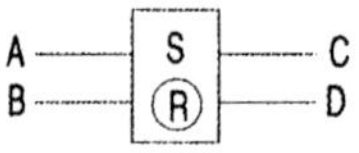 A ——[S]—— C B ——(R)—— D NOTE THAT INPUT B OVERRIDES INPUT A	DEFINITION: S REPRESENTS SET MEMORY AND R REPRESENTS RESET MEMORY. OUTPUT C EXISTS AS SOON AS INPUT A EXISTS AND CONTINUES TO EXIST REGARDLESS OF THE SUBSEQUENT STATE OF A, UNTIL RESET BY THE EXISTENCE OF INPUT B. C REMAINS TERMINATED REGARDLESS OF THE SUBSEQUENT STATE OF B, UNTIL THE LOGIC IS SET BY A. IF TANK T-16 PRESSURE IS HIGH, OPEN VALVE PV-38, CONTINUE VENTING REGARDLESS OF PRESSURE UNTIL VALVE IS CLOSED BY HS-3, PROVIDED THAT THE PRESSURE IS NOT HIGH. WHEN VENTING HAS STOPPED, PUMP P-7 SHOULD BE STARTED. 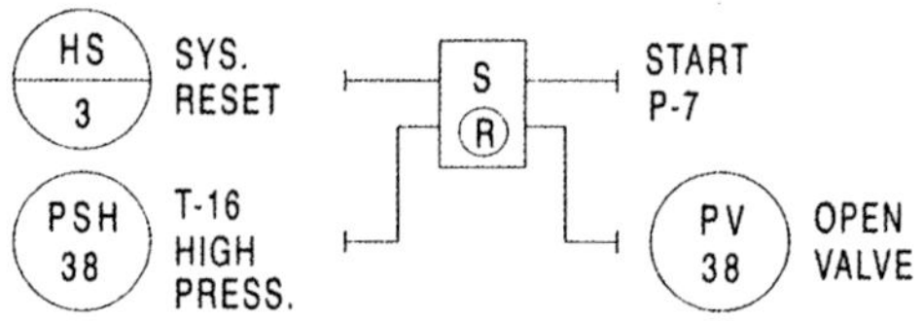 HS 3 SYS. RESET — S (R) — START P-7 PSH 38 T-16 HIGH PRESS. — PV 38 OPEN VALVE --- TRUTH TABLE SHOWING NEED FOR OVERRIDE. (truth table below) NOTES: * UNDEFINED ** DETERMINED BY LAST INPUT SIGNAL

TRUTH TABLE SHOWING NEED FOR OVERRIDE.

	INPUTS		OUTPUTS	
	A	B	C	D
WITHOUT OVERRIDE	1	1	*	*
	1	0	1	0
	0	1	0	1
	0	0	**	**
OVERRIDE ON INPUT B	1	1	0	1
	1	0	1	0
	0	1	0	1
	0	0	**	**

FIGURE 8-16 (cont.)
ISA logic symbols.

not just the logic. Power can fail at many points—input, output, a motor, a pneumatic or hydraulic power supply—and each of them must be considered. The authors do not favor use of these options.

Last, logic should never be "maybe." The truth table shows why the override should always be used.

The Time Elements

The authors can do no better than to refer the reader to ISA-5.2 for an excellent presentation of the time elements. Figures 8-17 and 8-18 reproduce the time elements from the standard.

Figure 8-17 gives the basic time elements, i.e., those that the reader will find useful for the major part of his or her work. Notice that there are only three basic time elements: Delayed Initiation of output, Delayed Termination of output, and Pulsed Output.

SYMBOL	DEFINITION	EXAMPLE
a) A ⊢—[*]—⊣ B * FOR FUNCTIONAL DETAILS, SEE THE FOLLOWING.	LOGIC OUTPUT B EXISTS WITH A TIME RELATIONSHIP TO LOGIC INPUT A AS SPECIFIED.	
b) A ⊢—[DI t]—⊣ B (DELAY INITIATION OF OUTPUT)	THE CONTINUOUS EXISTENCE OF LOGIC OUTPUT A FOR TIME t CAUSES LOGIC OUTPUT B TO EXIST WHEN t EXPIRES. B TERMINATES WHEN A TERMINATES.	IF REACTOR TEMPERATURE EXCEEDS A HIGH LIMIT CONTINUOUSLY FOR 10 SECONDS, BLOCK CATALYST FLOW. RESUME FLOW WHEN TEMPERATURE DOES NOT EXCEED THE LIMIT. REACTOR TEMP. HIGH ⊢—[DI 10 S]—⊣ BLOCK CATALYST FLOW
c) A ⊢—[DI t]—⊣ B (DELAY TERMINATION OF OUTPUT)	THE EXISTENCE OF LOGIC INPUT A CAUSES LOGIC OUTPUT B TO EXIST IMMEDIATELY. B TERMINATES WHEN A HAS TERMINATED AND HAS NOT AGAIN EXISTED FOR TIME t.	IF SYSTEM PRESSURE FALLS BELOW A LOW LIMIT, OPERATE COMPRESSOR AT ONCE. STOP THE COMPRESSOR WHEN PRESSURE IS NOT LOW CONTINUOUSLY FOR ONE MINUTE. SYSTEM PRESS. LOW ⊢—[DT 1 MIN]—⊣ OPERATE COMPRESSOR
d) A ⊢—[PO t]—⊣ B (PULSE OUTPUT)	THE EXISTENCE OF LOGIC INPUT A REGARDLESS OF ITS SUBSEQUENT STATE, CAUSES LOGIC OUTPUT B TO EXIST IMMEDIATELY. B EXISTS FOR TIME t AND THEN TERMINATES.	IF VESSEL PURGE FAILS FOR ANY PERIOD OF TIME, OPERATE EVACUATION PUMP FOR 3 MINUTES AND THEN STOP THE PUMP. VESSEL PURGE FAILS ⊢—[PO 3 MIN]—⊣ OPERATE EVACUATION PUMP

FIGURE 8-17
ISA basic time elements.

Figure 8-18 gives a generalized method for diagramming all time functions. The reader is advised to study the definitions and the examples carefully, since they are a priceless resource for augmenting one's intellectual bag of tricks.

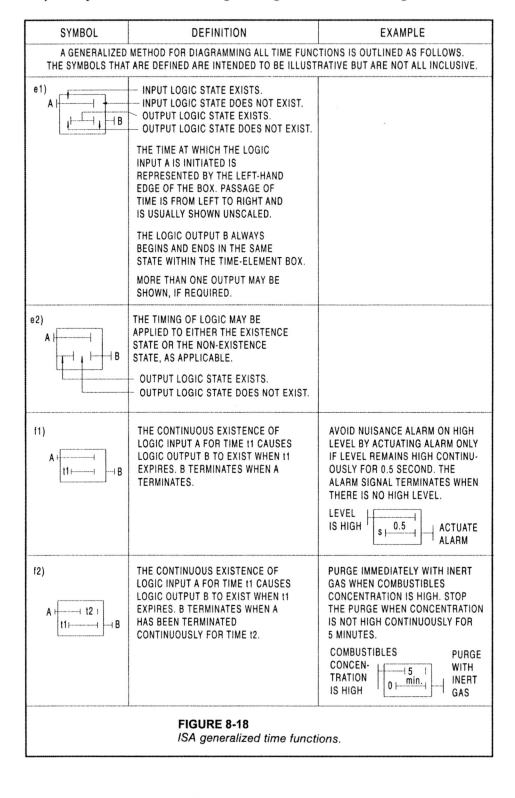

SYMBOL	DEFINITION	EXAMPLE
	A GENERALIZED METHOD FOR DIAGRAMMING ALL TIME FUNCTIONS IS OUTLINED AS FOLLOWS. THE SYMBOLS THAT ARE DEFINED ARE INTENDED TO BE ILLUSTRATIVE BUT ARE NOT ALL INCLUSIVE.	
e1)	─── INPUT LOGIC STATE EXISTS. ─── INPUT LOGIC STATE DOES NOT EXIST. ─── OUTPUT LOGIC STATE EXISTS. ─── OUTPUT LOGIC STATE DOES NOT EXIST. THE TIME AT WHICH THE LOGIC INPUT A IS INITIATED IS REPRESENTED BY THE LEFT-HAND EDGE OF THE BOX. PASSAGE OF TIME IS FROM LEFT TO RIGHT AND IS USUALLY SHOWN UNSCALED. THE LOGIC OUTPUT B ALWAYS BEGINS AND ENDS IN THE SAME STATE WITHIN THE TIME-ELEMENT BOX. MORE THAN ONE OUTPUT MAY BE SHOWN, IF REQUIRED.	
e2)	THE TIMING OF LOGIC MAY BE APPLIED TO EITHER THE EXISTENCE STATE OR THE NON-EXISTENCE STATE, AS APPLICABLE. ─── OUTPUT LOGIC STATE EXISTS. ─── OUTPUT LOGIC STATE DOES NOT EXIST.	
f1)	THE CONTINUOUS EXISTENCE OF LOGIC INPUT A FOR TIME t1 CAUSES LOGIC OUTPUT B TO EXIST WHEN t1 EXPIRES. B TERMINATES WHEN A TERMINATES.	AVOID NUISANCE ALARM ON HIGH LEVEL BY ACTUATING ALARM ONLY IF LEVEL REMAINS HIGH CONTINU- OUSLY FOR 0.5 SECOND. THE ALARM SIGNAL TERMINATES WHEN THERE IS NO HIGH LEVEL.
f2)	THE CONTINUOUS EXISTENCE OF LOGIC INPUT A FOR TIME t1 CAUSES LOGIC OUTPUT B TO EXIST WHEN t1 EXPIRES. B TERMINATES WHEN A HAS BEEN TERMINATED CONTINUOUSLY FOR TIME t2.	PURGE IMMEDIATELY WITH INERT GAS WHEN COMBUSTIBLES CONCENTRATION IS HIGH. STOP THE PURGE WHEN CONCENTRATION IS NOT HIGH CONTINUOUSLY FOR 5 MINUTES.

FIGURE 8-18
ISA generalized time functions.

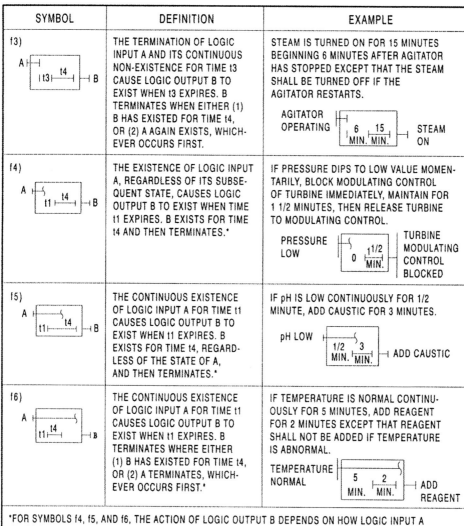

SYMBOL	DEFINITION	EXAMPLE
f3)	THE TERMINATION OF LOGIC INPUT A AND ITS CONTINUOUS NON-EXISTENCE FOR TIME t3 CAUSE LOGIC OUTPUT B TO EXIST WHEN t3 EXPIRES. B TERMINATES WHEN EITHER (1) B HAS EXISTED FOR TIME t4, OR (2) A AGAIN EXISTS, WHICHEVER OCCURS FIRST.	STEAM IS TURNED ON FOR 15 MINUTES BEGINNING 6 MINUTES AFTER AGITATOR HAS STOPPED EXCEPT THAT THE STEAM SHALL BE TURNED OFF IF THE AGITATOR RESTARTS.
f4)	THE EXISTENCE OF LOGIC INPUT A, REGARDLESS OF ITS SUBSEQUENT STATE, CAUSES LOGIC OUTPUT B TO EXIST WHEN TIME t1 EXPIRES. B EXISTS FOR TIME t4 AND THEN TERMINATES.*	IF PRESSURE DIPS TO LOW VALUE MOMENTARILY, BLOCK MODULATING CONTROL OF TURBINE IMMEDIATELY, MAINTAIN FOR 1 1/2 MINUTES, THEN RELEASE TURBINE TO MODULATING CONTROL.
f5)	THE CONTINUOUS EXISTENCE OF LOGIC INPUT A FOR TIME t1 CAUSES LOGIC OUTPUT B TO EXIST WHEN t1 EXPIRES. B EXISTS FOR TIME t4, REGARDLESS OF THE STATE OF A, AND THEN TERMINATES.*	IF pH IS LOW CONTINUOUSLY FOR 1/2 MINUTE, ADD CAUSTIC FOR 3 MINUTES.
f6)	THE CONTINUOUS EXISTENCE OF LOGIC INPUT A FOR TIME t1 CAUSES LOGIC OUTPUT B TO EXIST WHEN t1 EXPIRES. B TERMINATES WHERE EITHER (1) B HAS EXISTED FOR TIME t4, OR (2) A TERMINATES, WHICHEVER OCCURS FIRST.*	IF TEMPERATURE IS NORMAL CONTINUOUSLY FOR 5 MINUTES, ADD REAGENT FOR 2 MINUTES EXCEPT THAT REAGENT SHALL NOT BE ADDED IF TEMPERATURE IS ABNORMAL.

*FOR SYMBOLS f4, f5, AND f6, THE ACTION OF LOGIC OUTPUT B DEPENDS ON HOW LOGIC INPUT A IS IN CONTINUOUS EXISTENCE, UP TO THE LINE BREAK FOR A. BEYOND THE BREAK IN A, THE STATE OF A IS NOT SIGNIFICANT TO THE COMPLETION OF THE B SEQUENCE.

IF IT IS DESIRED TO HAVE A B TIME SEGMENT, E.G., t1, GO TO COMPLETION ONY IF A EXISTS CONTINUOUSLY, THEN A MUST BE DRAWN BEYOND THAT SEGMENT. IF A IS DRAWN PAST THE BEGINNING BUT NOT BEYOND THE END OF A TIME, THE SEGMENT WILL BE INITIATED AND GO TO COMPLETION REGARDLESS OF WHETHER A EXISTS ONLY MOMENTARILY OR LONGER.

STATEMENT OF SPECIAL REQUIREMENTS	LOGIC OUTPUT B EXISTS WITH A RELATIONSHIP TO LOGIC INPUT A AS SPECIFIED IN THE STATEMENT OF SPECIAL REQUIREMENTS. THE STATEMENT MAY COVER A LOGIC FUNCTION NOT OTHERWISE SPECIFIED IN THIS STANDARD OR A LOGIC SYSTEM THAT IS FURTHER DEFINED ELSEWHERE.

FIGURE 8-18 (cont.)
ISA generalized time functions.

▓ SUMMARY

The control systems engineer deals with binary logic. Binary means possessing one of two possible states such as ON or OFF. A logic system always presents the same set of outputs for the same set of inputs, although the output responses may be modified by some internal program.

Programmable controllers are replacing relay logic. Similar ladder diagrams are used to program both kinds of logic.

Binary logic diagramming simplifies and generalizes logic symbols. It also reduces the amount of hardware dependence.

The two major phases in accomplishing a workable control system are conceptualization and execution. The first phase should be hardware-independent, while the second need not necessarily be independent of the hardware chosen to execute the control scheme.

Also, two major types of documentation are associated with the two phases. The conceptual document attempts to depict a control scheme in the abstract. Its purpose is to help the designer, and all who need to see the larger picture, conceive of the scheme necessary to control the process. The execution document is aimed at instructing specialists on how to specifically develop a logic scheme that has already been decided upon in the abstract.

The conceptual document, of necessity, shows both the essential parts of the process and the operator interface. The execution document simply shows the inputs and the outputs. Ladder diagrams are execution documents.

Examples of function charts are given.

As far as timer elements are concerned, the descriptions given in ISA-5.2 are hard to improve upon.

The authors try to contrast what they consider good practice with some examples taken from the literature. Good practice can be measured both logically and aesthetically.

In logic diagramming it is very evident that one picture is worth more than a thousand words.

▓ QUESTIONS

1. Why should the result of a logical procedure never be 'maybe'?

2. Do you agree with the statement that logic is the art of non-contradictory identification?

3. Give a definition of the concept 'binary'.

4. Give a definition of 'logic' in terms of inputs and outputs.

5. What is the difference between combinatorial logic and sequential logic and why do the authors discount the difference?

6. Do you agree that there are two distinct phases in logic design? Name them.

7. Do you agree that the two phases drive the types of documents that are required?

8. Can you place all logic symbols on an EFD? If not, to what extend should logic be symbolized on an EFD?

9. Sketch a holding circuit using logic symbols.

10. Take another look at Zoss' batch reactor. Do you now agree that pictures are worth thousands of words?

11. Is ISA-5.2 an execution document or a conceptual document, in your opinion. What reasoning do the authors give for their opinion?

12. What are the major differences in style between conceptual documents and execution documents?

13. The authors give some pointers on what they consider good practice. There are eight points. Do you agree with them? Give your logical reasons for agreeing or disagreeing.

14. Why is it important to have a type of diagram that can be used for conceptual drawings that is independent of the hardware that will actually be used to implement the logic?

15. Explain some of the problems that can occur when sequential functions are implemented as in the Batch Chemical Reactor example. Why are retentive memory functions (flip-flops) useful in sequential control? Explain why retentive memory functions should not be used in interlocks involving safety.

16. Repeat the Batch Chemical Reactor example using sequential function charts. Which is easier to develop and easier to follow?

17. The conceptual diagrams in Chapter 8 use positive logic (an input device has to turn on to cause an action). Why would you not implement a STOP button in this manner?

REFERENCES

1. IEC 60848, (2002-02) GRAFCET Specification Language for Sequential Function Charts.

2. Zoss, L. M., 1979, *Applied Instrumentation in the Process Industries, Volume IV, Control Systems: Theory, Troubleshooting, and Design*, Houston, Gulf Publishing Company.

3. NF C03-190-TR1, French National Standards Commission Standard for Function Chart 'GRARFCET' for the Description of Logic Control Systems, 1995.

4. ANSI/IEEE Std. 91-1984, American National Standard for Graphic Symbols for Logic Diagrams (Two-State Devices).

5. NEMA, ICS1, 2000. Industrial Control and Systems: General Requirements.

9

LADDER DIAGRAMS AND WIRING DIAGRAMS

▩ INTRODUCTION: THE ELECTRICAL CONNECTION

There is a very heavy interface between the electrical discipline and the control systems discipline when it comes time for the execution of a control systems design. Since most instrumentation is now electrical in nature, implementation of control systems design is largely electrical in nature.

The above statement does not apply to the engineering design process itself, i.e., the bulk of control systems engineering work. Nor does it apply to the actual interface between the process being controlled and the control systems engineers, designers, and technicians. At this level the control systems engineer, for instance, has more in common with a process engineer than with an electrical engineer.

In spite of the closeness during detailed execution of design, control systems work and electrical work are sufficiently different, and each is sufficiently complex, to warrant two separate disciplines. As is usual when two closely related but different disciplines work together, careful attention must be paid to the interfaces between them. It is mainly at the interfaces that errors and problems occur.

This chapter will discuss those aspects of electrical symbolic representation that are most useful to control systems engineering and design personnel. The field of electrical engineering, design, and maintenance is vast; not all aspects of it are of direct interest to most control systems personnel. In this chapter are listed the standard types of drawings that a typical electrical department would issue along with examples and discussions of those particular drawings that are of direct interest and concern to most control systems personnel.

TABLE 9-1
Design Drawing List

1	Drawing Index
2	Drafting Symbols and Standard Notes
3	Area Classifications
4	One-line Diagrams
5	Standard Installation Assemblies
6	Grounding Drawings
7	Underground Conduit or Cable Drawings
8	Conduit Schedules
9	Cable or Circuit Schedules
10	Aboveground Power Drawings
11	Substation and Switch Gear Drawings
12	Lighting Drawings
13	Electrical Instrumentation Drawings
14	Control Building Drawings
15	Electrical Logic Drawings
16	Elementary (Ladder) Diagrams
17	Connection Diagrams
18	Pole-line Drawings
19	Miscellaneous Building Drawings
20	Heat Tracing Drawings
21	Nameplate Schedules

▓ ELECTRICAL WORK

Electrical work frequently is divided into two broad categories: power and control. More overlap occurs between electrical engineering and design and control systems engineering and design in the latter category. This is especially true of such modern technology as programmable controllers.

To give an idea of the breadth of electrical work, Table 9-1 gives a list of the design drawings that would be produced by a typical engineering and construction company's electrical department. In addition, electrical bills of material are often treated as drawings and are given a drawing number.

Of the drawings listed, the most important to control systems personnel are probably the Elementary (Ladder) Diagrams, Connection Diagrams, One-line Diagrams, and Area Classifications. More time is spent working with the first two: Ladder Diagrams and Connection Diagrams. This chapter will, therefore, place emphasis on these drawings while briefly discussing some of the others in the above list.

▓ DRAFTING SYMBOLS AND STANDARD NOTES

As always the legend sheet comes first after the drawing index. Each company has its own format, but the symbols used are generally based on ANSI and

SINGLE LINE	DETAILED DWG.	DEFINITION	NOTES
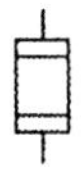	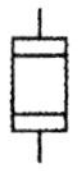	FUSE	SHOW RATING
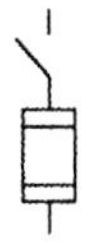	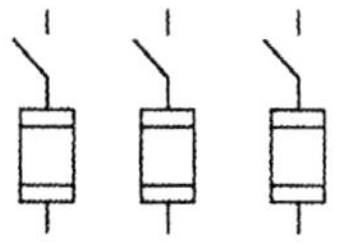	FUSED DISCONNECT	SHOW RATING
	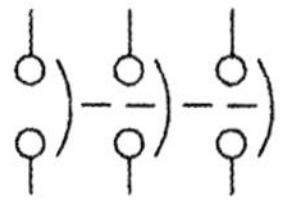	CIRCUIT BREAKER	SHOW TRIP SETTING AND FRAME SIZE
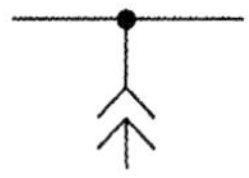	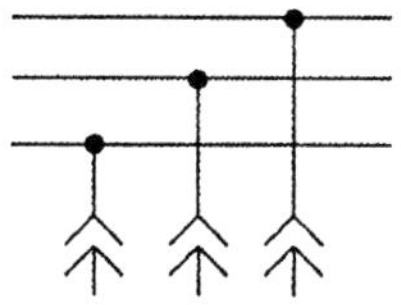	SEPARABLE CONNECTOR	COMBINATION STARTERS AND CIRCUIT BREAKERS IN MCCs
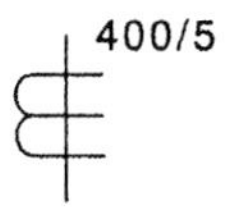 400/5	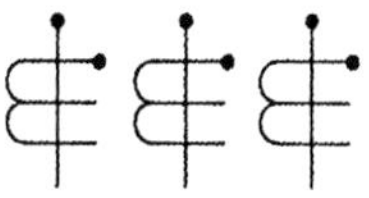	CURRENT TRANSFORMER	• POLARITY 400/5 IS WINDING RATIO
		POTENTIAL TRANSFORMERS	
		POWER TRANSFORMERS	◁ DELTA Y WYE ⏚ GROUND
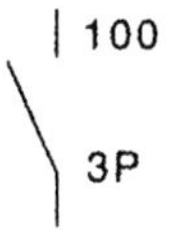 100 3P	 100	NONFUSIBLE DISCONNECT SWITCH	100 = AMPS 3P = 3-PHASE

(A) TYPICAL SYMBOLS

FIGURE 9-1
Typical electrical drawing legend sheet symbols.

NEMA standards. European practice differs rather radically from North American practice and it will not be discussed here.

Figure 9-1 shows typical symbols, definitions and notes that appear on most electrical drawing legend sheets. The beauty and importance of a legend sheet is that it gives the designer the building blocks with which to create complex

SYMBOL	DEFINITION	NOTES
START 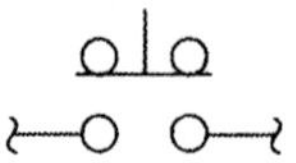	START PUSH BUTTON	MOMENTARY CONTACT
STOP 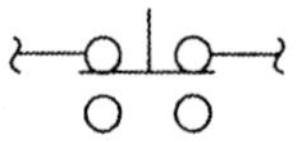	STOP PUSH BUTTON	MOMENTARY CONTACT
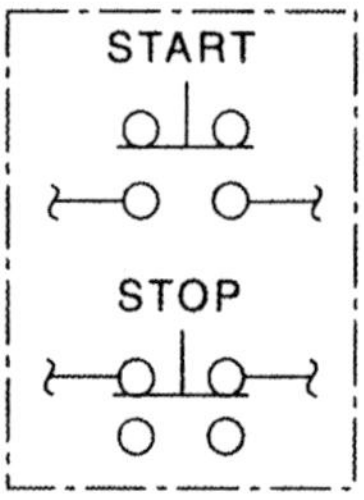 START STOP	COMBINED START AND STOP PUSH BUTTONS	INDEPENDENT FUNCTIONS (NOT MECHANICALLY CONNECTED)
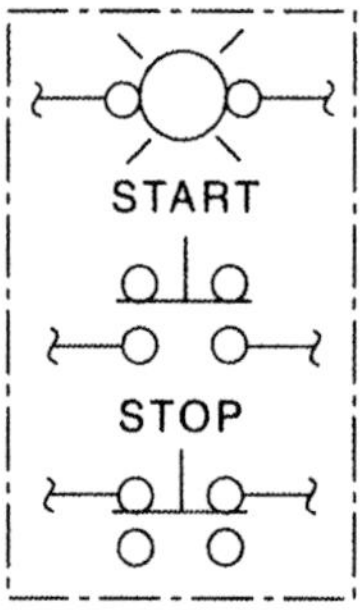 START STOP	COMBINED START AND STOP PUSH BUTTONS WITH INDICATING LIGHT	INDICATING LIGHT IS USUALLY "RUNNING" LIGHT CONNECTED TO RELAY IN CONTROL CIRCUIT
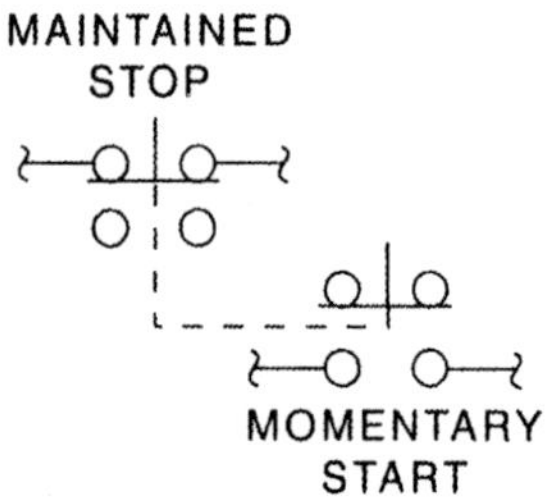 MAINTAINED STOP MOMENTARY START	MECHANICALLY LINKED PUSH BUTTON STATION	SPECIFY FUNCTIONS WITH WORDS
 R	INDICATING LIGHT	A - AMBER B - BLUE G - GREEN R - RED W - WHITE Y - YELLOW

(B) TYPICAL DEFINITIONS AND NOTES

FIGURE 9-1 (cont.)

SYMBOL	DEFINITION	NOTES
	NORMALLY OPEN (NO) CONTACT	"NORMALLY OPEN" REFERS TO SHELF POSITION
	NORMALLY CLOSED (NC) CONTACT	"NORMALLY CLOSED" REFERS TO SHELF POSITION
	THERMAL OVERLOAD CONTACT	
	MAGNETIC OVERLOAD CONTACT	CONTACTS SHOWN AS NC CONTACTS
	GROUND CONNECTION	FOLLOWS NEC RULES
TDO	TIME DELAY SWITCH	NC CONTACT WITH TIMED OPENING
TDC	TIME DELAY SWITCH	NO CONTACT WITH TIMED CLOSURE
R1 OR R1	OPERATING COIL, RELAY OR STARTER	DESIGNATION IS ACCORDING TO IDENTIFICATION SCHEME
+ 125 VDC	BATTERY	SHOW VOLTAGE AND POLARITY
(B) CONTINUED **FIGURE 9-1 (cont.)**		

designs. It also defines symbols and usage on a specific project. For instance, a note regarding pilot light colors could read, "G-to be used for 'Power Available,' 'Motor Stopped,' or 'Breaker Open.' R-to be used for 'Motor Running,' 'Breaker Closed,' or 'Alarm Condition'." When applied to motors, the opposite convention is sometimes used. Engineering companies sometimes have difficulty switching from one definition to another at the insistence of a particular client. The legend sheet is the place to eliminate ambiguity.

SYMBOL	DEFINITION	NOTES
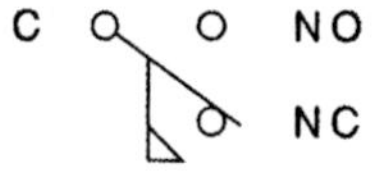 C ─○ ○ NO / ○ NC	FLOW SWITCH	NO, NC REFER TO SHELF POSITION
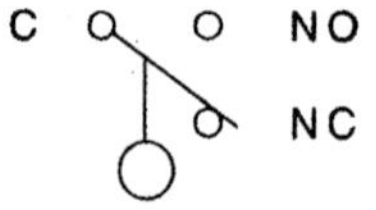 C ─○ ○ NO / ○ NC	LEVEL SWITCH	NO, NC REFER TO SHELF POSITION
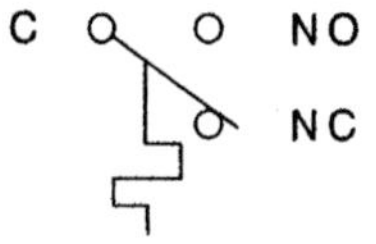 C ─○ ○ NO / ○ NC	TEMPERATURE SWITCH	NO, NC REFER TO SHELF POSITION
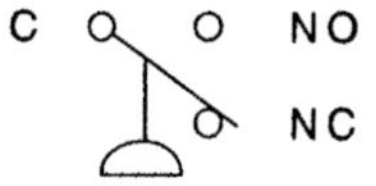 C ─○ ○ NO / ○ NC	PRESSURE/ VACUUM SWITCH	NO, NC REFER TO SHELF POSITION
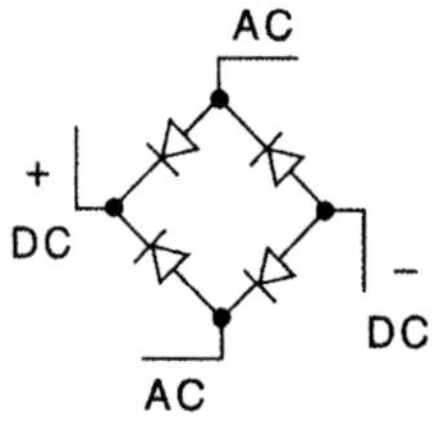 AC / + DC / − DC / AC	FULL WAVE RECTIFIER	DESIGNATE VOLTAGES

(B) CONTINUED

FIGURE 9-1 (cont.)

Another electrical legend sheet frequently called "Electrical Physical Drafting Symbols," is used for layout-type drawings. It is important for the understanding of the physical construction and layout of electrical conduit and cabling systems and is mentioned to emphasize the importance of the existence of legend sheets. An example is not shown because it has less interest from a strictly control systems point of view.

AREA CLASSIFICATION DRAWINGS

Area classification drawings simply define by shading and crosshatching the extent of electrically hazardous areas according to the NFPA code. They are usually made on plot plans and elevation drawings. Since they are not really electrical diagrams and sometimes are produced by other disciplines, they will not be further discussed.

▨ ONE-LINE DIAGRAMS

"Single Lines," as they are often called, show three-phase power distribution to equipment in a simplified manner—without leaving out any essential functional details. They show the incoming electrical service and usually define the extent of the electrical utility's responsibilities.

One-lines show switches and protective devices, circuit breakers, switchgear, transformers, potheads, motor controllers, motors and generators, metering equipment, relaying and controlling devices, push buttons, lighting panels, welding outlets, and miscellaneous loads such as heaters. They are to the electrical engineer what the engineering flow diagram is to the control systems and process engineer. They carry standard (electrical) symbols and equipment numbers, show equipment ratings, and indicate conduit or cable identification.

Figure 9-2 is an example of a one-line diagram. The flow of electrical power is top down, from the source to the user via the heavy solid lines. A single line (hence the name) is used to represent all three phases. The breakers are shown as simple contacts with one contact representing three. Circles, with standardized numbers specifying the function, represent the protective devices.

In the example, 4160-V AC power flows through a fused breaker with a control switch (see the legend—Table 9-2). The control switch and the associated red and green lights are powered by a transformer with fuses in the primary and secondary windings. The double arrows show that the breaker can be physically disconnected from both the incoming line and the down-stream equipment, including the control circuit and a voltmeter switch.

When the breaker is in place, power flows through the control switch transformer and the M coil may be activated by the control switch so that the 1200-amp bus can be energized. At any time the breaker is in place, the voltmeter switch can be used to check the voltage on any phase. The undervoltage relay (27) is connected to an alarm on an auxiliary panel (note the combination of electrical and instrumentation symbols).

Devices 51 and 46 are current relays that will trip the breaker on an overcurrent or on current imbalance. An ammeter switch allows monitoring of the current in each phase.

Below the main bus, power is distributed to motors in a manner similar to that as described above. From a control point of view, it is intriguing to see

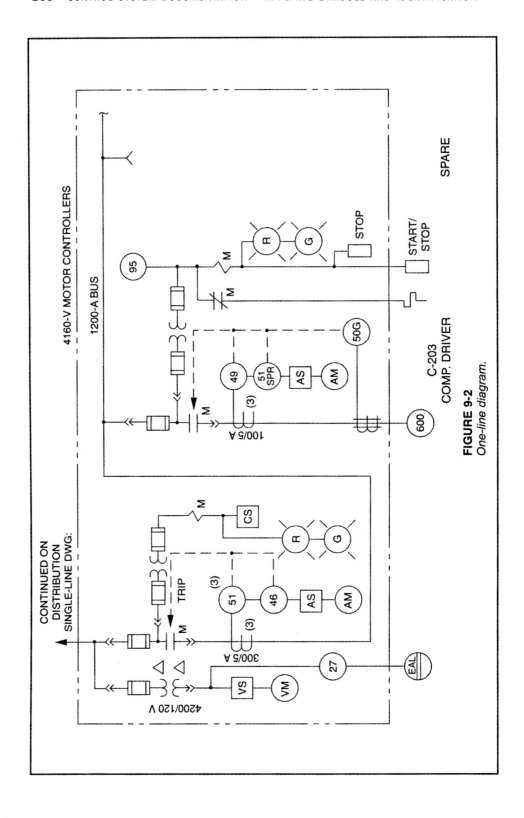

FIGURE 9-2
One-line diagram.

TABLE 9-2
Legend

26	Apparatus Thermal Device
27	Undervoltage Relay
46	Phase Balance Current Relay
49	Thermal Relay
50	Instantaneous Overcurrent or Rate-of-Rise Relay
51	AC Time Overcurrent Relay
63	Pressure Switch
95	Undervoltage Reacceleration Relay
SPR	Stalled Rotor Protection
AM	Ammeter
VM	Voltmeter
AS	Ammeter Switch
VS	Voltmeter Switch
CS	Control Switch
EAL	Undervoltage Alarm

that the motor heater is energized via a contact from the M coil only when the motor is stopped with the breaker racked in.

Most one-lines will contain much more information than does Figure 9-2, and the typical legend shown in Table 9-2 will be much more extensive. However, the figure and the above description are a good example of the wealth of information that can be conveyed in a very simple format.

▧ STANDARD INSTALLATION ASSEMBLIES

Figure 9-3 is an example of a standard installation assembly drawing. These drawings are very much akin to the instrument installation detail except that they refer to electrical equipment. Like the instrument detail drawing, they have a closely associated "bill of materials" (material list). These details are quite extensive. They cover instrument installation, junction box installation, recommended electrical installation practices, cable tray installation, motor installations (above and below ground), grounding details, lighting installations, panel board installation assemblies, and support (of all kinds) installations.

A similar approach is taken to electrical installation details. The drawings are simplified to an extreme, there are no unnecessary lines, numbered flags are used to identify written descriptions, and lead from flags are only connected at the circle end.

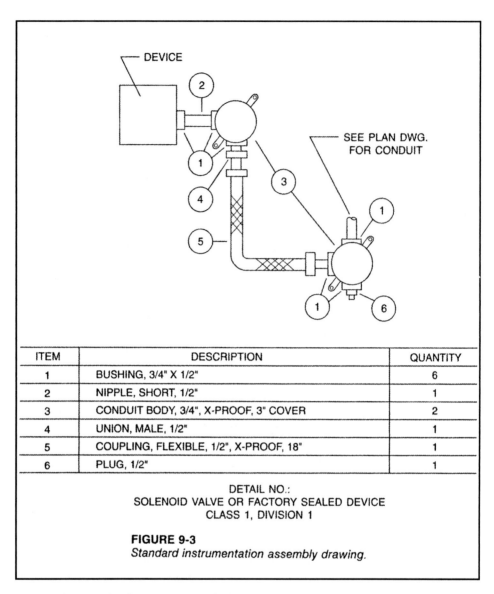

ITEM	DESCRIPTION	QUANTITY
1	BUSHING, 3/4" X 1/2"	6
2	NIPPLE, SHORT, 1/2"	1
3	CONDUIT BODY, 3/4", X-PROOF, 3" COVER	2
4	UNION, MALE, 1/2"	1
5	COUPLING, FLEXIBLE, 1/2", X-PROOF, 18"	1
6	PLUG, 1/2"	1

DETAIL NO.:
SOLENOID VALVE OR FACTORY SEALED DEVICE
CLASS 1, DIVISION 1

FIGURE 9-3
Standard instrumentation assembly drawing.

The preference for format is for a full-sized drawing with the bill of materials directly under the drawing so that the key numbers can be easily located. This is unlike the preference for the 8-1/2 by 11 format associated with the instrument installation detail.

▥ GROUNDING DRAWINGS

Electrical grounding drawings are quite complex. They are of two types: one is similar to an installation detail and consists of a series of individual equipment details; the other is a layout-type drawing that shows location, connection points, and routing of cables. These drawings will not be shown as they are of

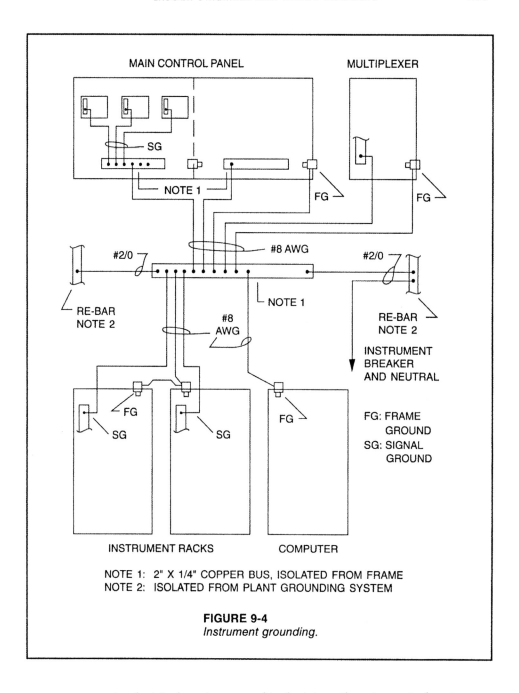

FIGURE 9-4
Instrument grounding.

more concern to electrical engineers and technicians than to control systems personnel.

Electrical engineers and designers are concerned with safety since their work involves high voltage and heavy currents. Control systems engineers and designers are also concerned with safety, but they are also concerned with the reduction of electrical noise. Figure 9-4 shows that the frame grounds (safety grounds) are isolated from the signal grounds (noise) until they meet at the large (2 inches by 1/4 inch) copper node bus. This bus is connected to the ground loop via 2/0 conductors.

Notice that the instrument power neutral is tied to the instrument ground loop separately at the point of least resistance. Notice also that the instrument ground is isolated from the plant (electrical) ground loop system. This drawing presents much information in a very simple manner.

▨ LADDER DIAGRAMS/ELEMENTARY DIAGRAMS

Ladder diagrams are electrical "binary control" diagrams. They were originally developed for relay logic; then they were modified for programmable control logic. In the first case, they represent physical devices; in the second, they represent the functions that solid-state devices perform, not necessarily the devices themselves. Since they are "binary" in nature, i.e., possessing two states, they are ideal for depicting binary or on-off logic. They are fairly straightforward and easy to understand.

The Allen-Bradley® publication, Bulletin 800 [Ref. 1], gives good examples of ladder diagrams combined with the associated push button wiring diagram. Figures 9-5 through 9-8 are taken directly from this publication. The drawings and the accompanying narrative are sufficiently clear and warrant no further comment.

Figure 9-9 is an example of the combination of elementary and connection diagrams normally used in industry to depict motor control. This type of drawing allows an understanding of the control logic, and it fixes the locations and terminal numbers of all the essential devices.

The drawing consists of two sections: the left-hand side is a physical representation of the components and their interconnecting wiring: the right- hand side is a functional schematic drawing.

On the schematic portion of the drawing, the solid lines represent wiring that is internal to the MCC cubicle. The dashed lines represent wiring external to the cubicle, i.e., wiring that the field installation electrician would have to install. These are the wiring to the motor T leads and the three wires to the control station. The drawing shows one of the most basic types of electrical motor control circuits, but it contains all of the essentials.

This booklet is designed to serve as:

1. An aid in the understanding of control circuits.
2. A handy reference, to point out the features of the more common circuits.
3. An aid in the selection and installation of push button stations.

NOTE: The symbols used in this booklet were adapted by Allen Bradley for use in all its publications. They are in accordance with NEMA standards. A particular application must satisfy the needs of the user and comply with applicable codes and laws, before using any of the typical circuits shown in this publication.

Each circuit is illustrated with a control circuit schematic or line diagram and a push button station wiring diagram.

The schematic or line diagram includes all components of the control circuit and indicates their function.

The push button station wiring diagram is a representation of the physical station, showing the relative positions of units, the suggested internal wiring, and connections with the starter.

Symbols common to most circuits are explained below; less common symbols are explained where they occur.

EXPLANATION OF SYMBOLS

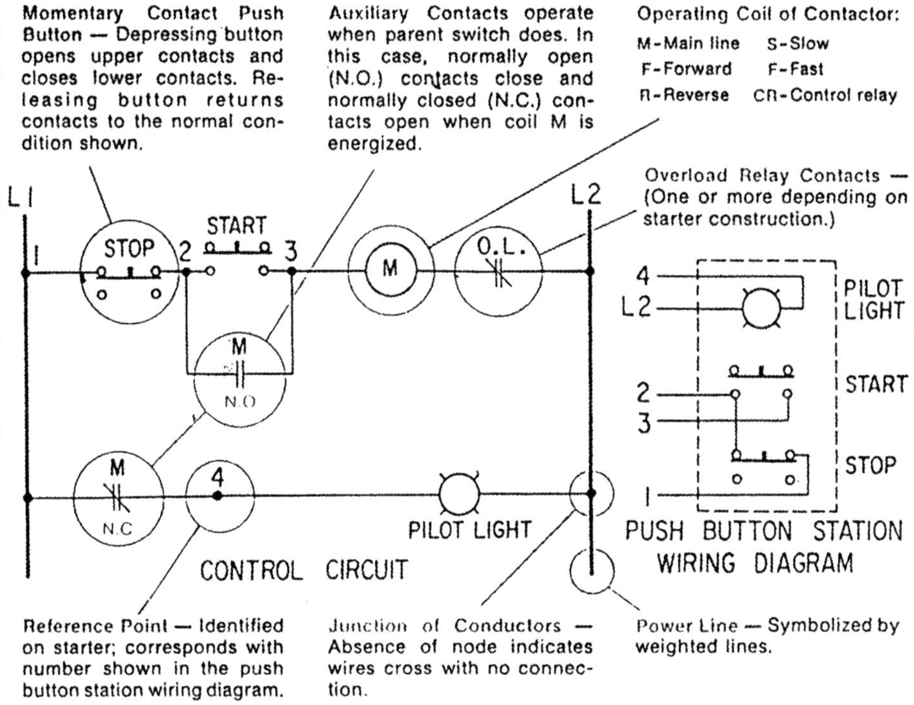
Momentary Contact Push Button — Depressing button opens upper contacts and closes lower contacts. Releasing button returns contacts to the normal condition shown.
Auxiliary Contacts operate when parent switch does. In this case, normally open (N.O.) contacts close and normally closed (N.C.) contacts open when coil M is energized.
Operating Coil of Contactor:
M-Main line S-Slow
F-Forward F-Fast
R-Reverse CR-Control relay
Overload Relay Contacts — (One or more depending on starter construction.)
L1
L2
1
STOP
2
START
3
M
O.L.
M
N.O
M
N.C
4
PILOT LIGHT
CONTROL CIRCUIT
4
L2
PILOT LIGHT
START
2
3
STOP
1
PUSH BUTTON STATION WIRING DIAGRAM
Reference Point — Identified on starter; corresponds with number shown in the push button station wiring diagram.
Junction of Conductors — Absence of node indicates wires cross with no connection.
Power Line — Symbolized by weighted lines.

FIGURE 9-5
A-B push button wiring diagrams. (Courtesy Allen-Bradley)

SINGLE STATION — BASIC CIRCUIT

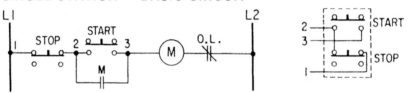

Operation — Pushing the start button energizes coil M; hold-in contacts M close, and maintain the circuit after the start button is released. Pushing the stop button breaks the circuit, de-energizing coil M; contacts M return to their normally open position.

Overload Protection — Operation of the overload relay contacts breaks the circuit, thus opens contacts M. To restart the motor the overloads must be reset and the start button must again be depressed.

Undervoltage Protection — If a power failure de-energizes the circuit, hold-in contacts M open. This protects against the motor starting automatically after the power returns. Unless otherwise stated, circuits to follow incorporate Undervoltage Protection.

SINGLE STATION — WITH MOTOR RUNNING PILOT LIGHT

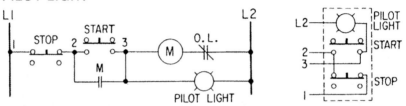

Whenever the motor is running, the pilot light is lit. Except for this modification, the circuit and its operation is the same as the basic single station.

SINGLE STATION — WITH MOTOR RUNNING PUSH-TO-TEST PILOT LIGHT

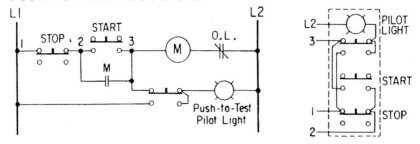

This circuit includes a running push-to-test pilot light which is wired to an independent test circuit. The bulb may be tested for burn-out easily and quickly — by simply depressing the lens.

FIGURE 9-6
A-B start-stop control wiring diagrams.
(Courtesy Allen-Bradley)

SINGLE STATION —WITH MOTOR STOPPED PILOT LIGHT

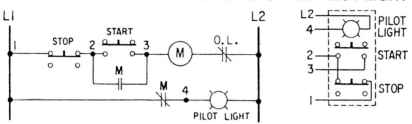

Normally closed auxiliary contacts such as the Bulletin 1495 are required. With the motor running, these contacts are open; with the motor stopped, they are closed and the pilot light is lit. Except for this modification, the circuit and its operation is the same as the basic circuit on Page 4.

GROUP OF SINGLE STATIONS — WITH MASTER STOP BUTTON

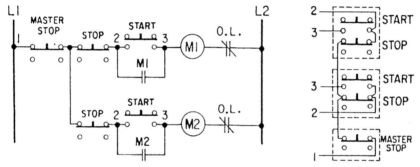

A momentary contact master stop is connected in series with a group of parallel connected circuits. Depressing the button de-energizes all of the circuits.

The circuits above are the basic start-stop circuit shown on Page 4; they could just as well be any of the preceding or following circuits which provide under-voltage protection. Two wire control or undervoltage release circuits are not applicable because they would be re-energized as soon as the master stop button is released.

SINGLE STATION — MAINTAINED CONTACT BUTTONS

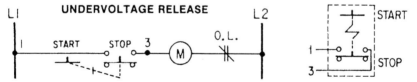

The start button mechanically maintains the contacts that take the place of hold-in contacts. Depressing the start button maintains the circuit; depressing the stop button breaks the circuit by opening the start contacts.

If the contactor is de-energized by a power failure or overload operation, the start contacts are unaffected. The motor restarts automatically.

FIGURE 9-7
A-B start-stop control wiring diagrams.
(Courtesy Allen-Bradley)

MULTI-STATION — WITH MOMENTARY CONTACT PUSH BUTTONS

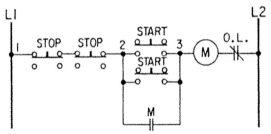
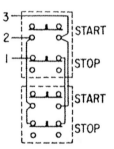

Operation — The motor may be started or stopped from a number of separate stations by connecting the start buttons in parallel and the stop buttons in series. Operation of each station is the same as with the basic circuit on Page 4.

Pilot Lights — It is possible to add motor running, stopped, or push-to-test pilot lights to any or all stations by connecting the lights to the circuit as shown below. Catalog numbers of the required push button stations are listed in the appropriate pilot light circuits on Pages 4 and 5.

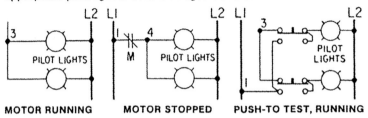

MOTOR RUNNING   MOTOR STOPPED   PUSH-TO TEST, RUNNING

MULTI-STATION — WITH MOMENTARY START-MAINTAINED STOP PUSH BUTTONS

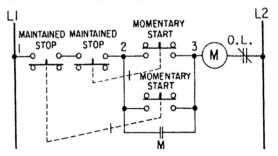
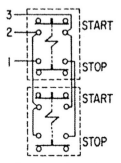

This circuit is identical to the one above; the stop buttons, however, have maintained contacts which are closed mechanically, by pressing the corresponding start button. This circuit is designed to permit stopping the motor from either station — but starting the motor only from the station at which it was stopped.

The start buttons are momentary contact; hold-in contacts-M provide undervoltage protection as with the preceding circuits.

FIGURE 9-8
A-B start-stop control wiring diagrams.
(Courtesy Allen-Bradley)

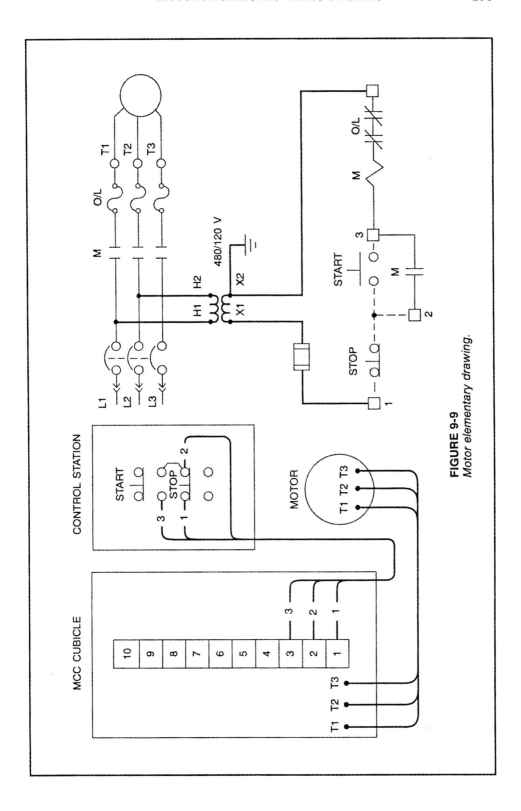

FIGURE 9-9
Motor elementary drawing.

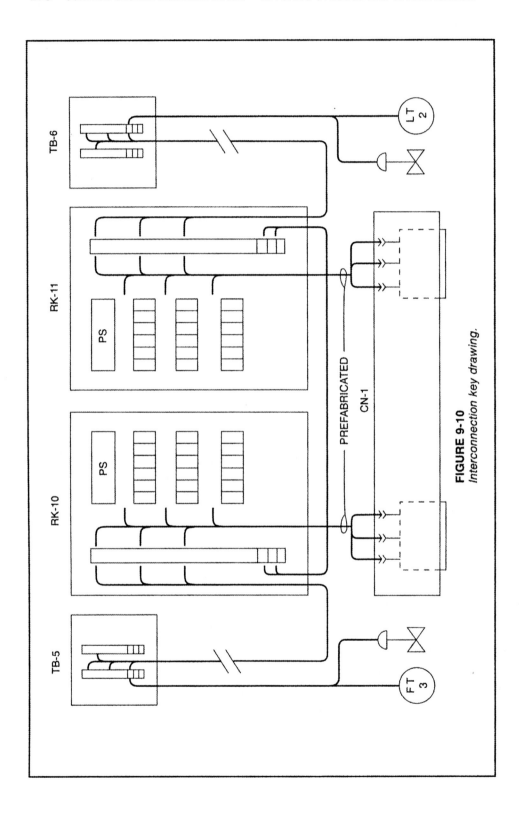

FIGURE 9-10
Interconnection key drawing.

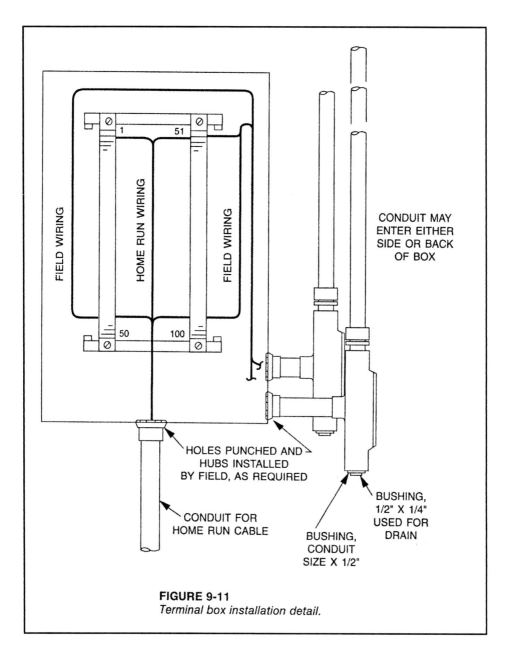

FIGURE 9-11
Terminal box installation detail.

Figure 9-10 is a typical electrical interconnection scheme. Its purpose is to serve as a key for understanding complex components. It shows that field-mounted control valves and transmitters are connected to two separate field junction boxes. Two home run cables are connected to rack terminal strips in two separate racks. The racks are interconnected, and prefabricated cable sets tie control panel instruments to the racks. Sufficient identification is included to permit the reader to grasp the overall approach and to see where more detailed drawings such as loop diagrams fit the larger scheme.

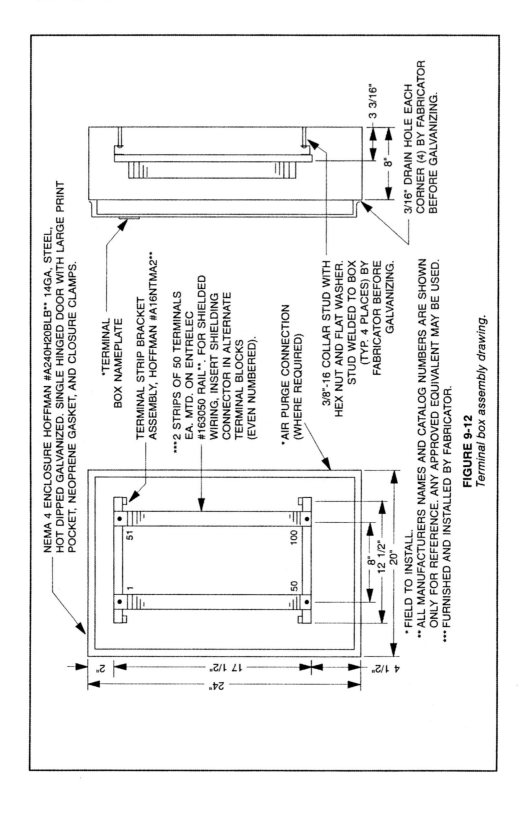

FIGURE 9-12
Terminal box assembly drawing.

Figure 9-11 is an electrical installation detail for a field terminal box. It carries much information with very few words. Conduit connections are at the bottom to preserve the integrity of the top of the box (to ensure no entry of water). Home run wiring is in the center of the two strips; field wiring is on the outside. Figure 9-12 is an assembly instruction drawing for the box itself.

▨ SUMMARY

The subject of electrical symbols and identification is worthy of a book in itself. The authors have always admired the simplicity of electrical symbols and the fashion in which the use of these symbols is used to convey a great deal of detailed information.

This chapter only touches upon those aspects of electrical symbolism that are of greatest concern to the control systems engineer and designer. Of the two basic divisions of electrical work (power and control), only the latter is addressed. A listing is given, however, of the typical standard drawings that an electrical department would produce in order to show the scope of work on a typical project.

The legend sheet is presented as always being paramount in any series of drawings. One-line diagrams are given as an example of power distribution, from a functional point of view, with the associated controls. Several paragraphs explain the details, not because the authors wished to be pedantic, but because so much information is conveyed in such a simple fashion that it is worth examining the details. Standard electrical installation assemblies are likened to instrument installation details. Electrical grounding drawings are contrasted to instrument grounding drawings, and the safety/noise dichotomy is highlighted.

Finally, ladder diagrams and elementary diagrams, the meat of the matter as far as control systems personnel are concerned, are discussed. Allen-Bradley® push button schematics are shown as good examples of information transfer. A typical elementary and connection diagram is given, and the last sequence of drawings depicts interconnection schemes and junction box wiring and arrangement details.

▨ QUESTIONS

1. Why is the interface between instrument and electrical designers heavier than that between instrument and electrical engineers?

2. With what other engineering discipline does the controls systems engineer have the greatest interface in the process industries? Why?

3. What are the to broad categories of electrical work? Where do control systems personnel fit in to the two categories?

4. Which are the electrical drawings of primary interest to control systems personnel?

5. Again, why does the author use words such as 'beauty and importance' when talking about legend sheets?

6. In your opinion, is an area classification drawing really an electrical drawing? If the electrical engineering design department produces it, what other disciplines should have an input to its content?

7. What is the other name for a single-line drawing? What is its purpose? To what other engineering drawing is it likened?

8. What are the similarities between electrical and instrument installation details? What is the major difference?

9. What are the two major purposes of electrical grounding?

10. What was the original purpose of a ladder diagram? How has it been adapted to newer technology?

11. Why is the control systems engineer or the instrument designer concerned with ladder diagrams for motor control?

REFERENCE

1. Bulletin 800, *Typical Wiring Diagrams for Push Button Stations*, Publication 800- 2.0 November 1977, pp. 2-6,
   http://domino.automation.rockwell.com/Applications/kb/kb.nsf/Ø/7ea9Ø11
   Milwaukee, WI: Allen-Bradley.

10

INSTALLATION DETAILS

▦ INTRODUCTION: PUTTING IT ALL TOGETHER

Installation details give specific instructions, in a very concise manner, to a technician on how to install a specific instrument and its related equipment. Each individual detail is usually accompanied by an associated bill of materials, which identifies specifically each item on the installation detail.

A drawing of the same style is used for transmitting fabrication instructions to maintenance shops and vendors. Therefore, this kind of drawing will also be discussed in this chapter.

▦ FORMAT AND STYLE

The format for an instrument installation detail is usually 8-1/2 inches by 11 inches for convenience to the installer (who installs only one item at a time). Sometimes the accompanying bill of materials is a separate 8-1/2 by 11 printout, and sometimes the two documents are printed side by side on the same 11 by 17 inch piece of paper. In either case, the numbering system should allow the bill of materials to be easily tied to the installation detail.

It is not wise to use a larger format nor to combine more than one detail on the same document. One should always keep the end user in mind. There are exceptions to the foregoing rule, as will be seen from the first few examples. The main exception occurs when the sheet is an instruction document for engineering office use.

The drawing style is either orthogonal or isometric. An isometric style allows relative locations to be portrayed. At the same time, it allows the installer considerable freedom in the choice of dimensions.

Drawing numbers differ from company to company. The important thing is not the number per se, but the fact that the number is referenced in the instrument index. The installation subcontractor will (1) first check the Engineering Flow Diagram to see the general details of what is to be installed, (2) look up the instrument by its tag number in the Instrument Index, (3) find the detail or details that are applicable, and (4) install the instrument according to the instructions given on the Instrument Installation Detail(s).

Regardless of whether there is a detail for each instrument or if use has been made of typical details, the Instrument Index will carry the information required to find the detail(s) necessary to install the instrument.

As usual, a new series of drawings covering a specific area requires its own legend sheet. Figure 10-1 is an example of one company's legend sheet. The size is 8-1/2 by 11 for the reasons given above.

In spite of the usual rule of one drawing for each instrument, a few drawings do contain more than one detail. Figure 10-2 is such an example. The figure gives typical mounting details for pedestals and other supports.

Another drawing that deviates from the above rule is Figure 10-3, which shows a general isometric of an instrument air system. This drawing represents the value of a document that is specific enough to cover details that should not be missed—for instance, the takeoffs from the top of the main header to avoid dirt and any possible condensation entering the branch lines. It is also general enough to allow field choice of routing and distance between instrument air users.

Figure 10-4 is a similar isometric that covers general instructions for impulse tubing protection and support.

Installation details are often used for information transfer between disciplines. For instance, the simple flow sheet representation usually has to be translated into something more specific for complete installation. Before the instrument technician installs the instrument, the piping designer must have given instructions to have the piping spool fabricated, ready to receive the device. Figures 10-5 and 10-6 tell the designer how to interpret Engineering Flow Diagram symbols. This example shows the wealth of information that can be contained in simple flow sheet symbols.

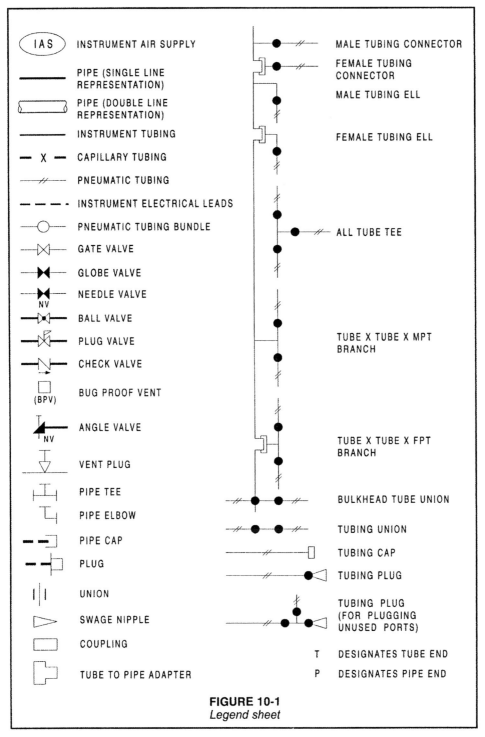

FIGURE 10-1
Legend sheet

Figure 10-7 shows the division of work and responsibility between the piping and the instrument disciplines with regard to an instrument air distribution system. Figures 10-8 through 10-10 define clearances for various instruments. All of these drawings are generally classified as "instrument details."

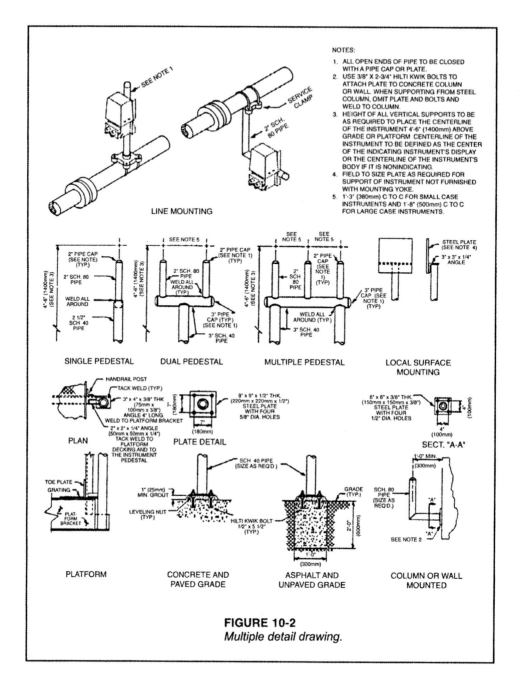

FIGURE 10-2
Multiple detail drawing.

▨ DRAWINGS BY CATEGORIES OF INSTRUMENTS

The following are examples of installation details categorized by type and function with some comments. This method of categorization is the way that work usually gets done. A design supervisor will usually have hundreds of drawings, collected over the years, all categorized in this fashion. When there is a new installation, leafing through what has been done before in that

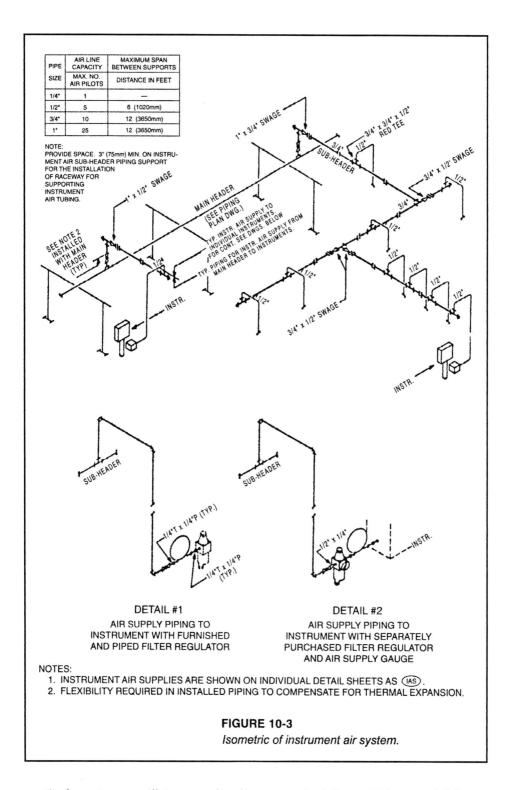

PIPE SIZE	AIR LINE CAPACITY MAX. NO. AIR PILOTS	MAXIMUM SPAN BETWEEN SUPPORTS DISTANCE IN FEET
1/4"	1	—
1/2"	5	6 (1020mm)
3/4"	10	12 (3650mm)
1"	25	12 (3650mm)

NOTE:
PROVIDE SPACE. 3" (75mm) MIN. ON INSTRU-MENT AIR SUB-HEADER PIPING SUPPORT FOR THE INSTALLATION OF RACEWAY FOR SUPPORTING INSTRUMENT AIR TUBING.

DETAIL #1
AIR SUPPLY PIPING TO INSTRUMENT WITH FURNISHED AND PIPED FILTER REGULATOR

DETAIL #2
AIR SUPPLY PIPING TO INSTRUMENT WITH SEPARATELY PURCHASED FILTER REGULATOR AND AIR SUPPLY GAUGE

NOTES:
1. INSTRUMENT AIR SUPPLIES ARE SHOWN ON INDIVIDUAL DETAIL SHEETS AS (IAS).
2. FLEXIBILITY REQUIRED IN INSTALLED PIPING TO COMPENSATE FOR THERMAL EXPANSION.

FIGURE 10-3
Isometric of instrument air system.

particular category will turn up the closest match. A few additions and deletions will produce a brand new installation detail.

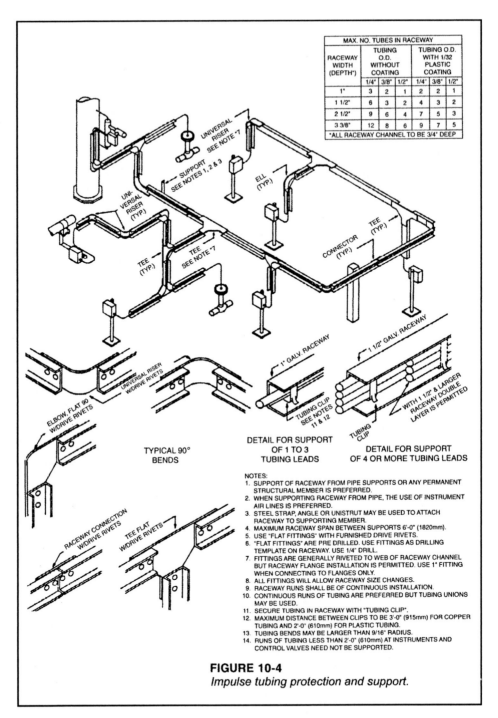

MAX. NO. TUBES IN RACEWAY						
RACEWAY WIDTH (DEPTH*)	TUBING O.D. WITHOUT COATING			TUBING O.D. WITH 1/32 PLASTIC COATING		
	1/4"	3/8"	1/2"	1/4"	3/8"	1/2"
1"	3	2	1	2	2	1
1 1/2"	6	3	2	4	3	2
2 1/2"	9	6	4	7	5	3
3 3/8"	12	8	6	9	7	5

*ALL RACEWAY CHANNEL TO BE 3/4" DEEP

DETAIL FOR SUPPORT OF 1 TO 3 TUBING LEADS

TYPICAL 90° BENDS

DETAIL FOR SUPPORT OF 4 OR MORE TUBING LEADS

NOTES:
1. SUPPORT OF RACEWAY FROM PIPE SUPPORTS OR ANY PERMANENT STRUCTURAL MEMBER IS PREFERRED.
2. WHEN SUPPORTING RACEWAY FROM PIPE, THE USE OF INSTRUMENT AIR LINES IS PREFERRED.
3. STEEL STRAP, ANGLE OR UNISTRUT MAY BE USED TO ATTACH RACEWAY TO SUPPORTING MEMBER.
4. MAXIMUM RACEWAY SPAN BETWEEN SUPPORTS 6'-0" (1820mm).
5. USE "FLAT FITTINGS" WITH FURNISHED DRIVE RIVETS.
6. "FLAT FITTINGS" ARE PRE DRILLED. USE FITTINGS AS DRILLING TEMPLATE ON RACEWAY. USE 1/4" DRILL.
7. FITTINGS ARE GENERALLY RIVETED TO WEB OF RACEWAY CHANNEL BUT RACEWAY FLANGE INSTALLATION IS PERMITTED. USE 1" FITTING WHEN CONNECTING TO FLANGES ONLY.
8. ALL FITTINGS WILL ALLOW RACEWAY SIZE CHANGES.
9. RACEWAY RUNS SHALL BE OF CONTINUOUS INSTALLATION.
10. CONTINUOUS RUNS OF TUBING ARE PREFERRED BUT TUBING UNIONS MAY BE USED.
11. SECURE TUBING IN RACEWAY WITH "TUBING CLIP".
12. MAXIMUM DISTANCE BETWEEN CLIPS TO BE 3'-0" (915mm) FOR COPPER TUBING AND 2'-0" (610mm) FOR PLASTIC TUBING.
13. TUBING BENDS MAY BE LARGER THAN 9/16" RADIUS.
14. RUNS OF TUBING LESS THAN 2'-0" (610mm) AT INSTRUMENTS AND CONTROL VALVES NEED NOT BE SUPPORTED.

FIGURE 10-4
Impulse tubing protection and support.

Orifice Flow Instruments

Flow instruments using orifice plates are among the most common type of instrument that requires an installation detail. Figure 10-11 is an example of an installation detail for the process piping (impulse lines) only of a line-mounted flow transmitter on liquid service.

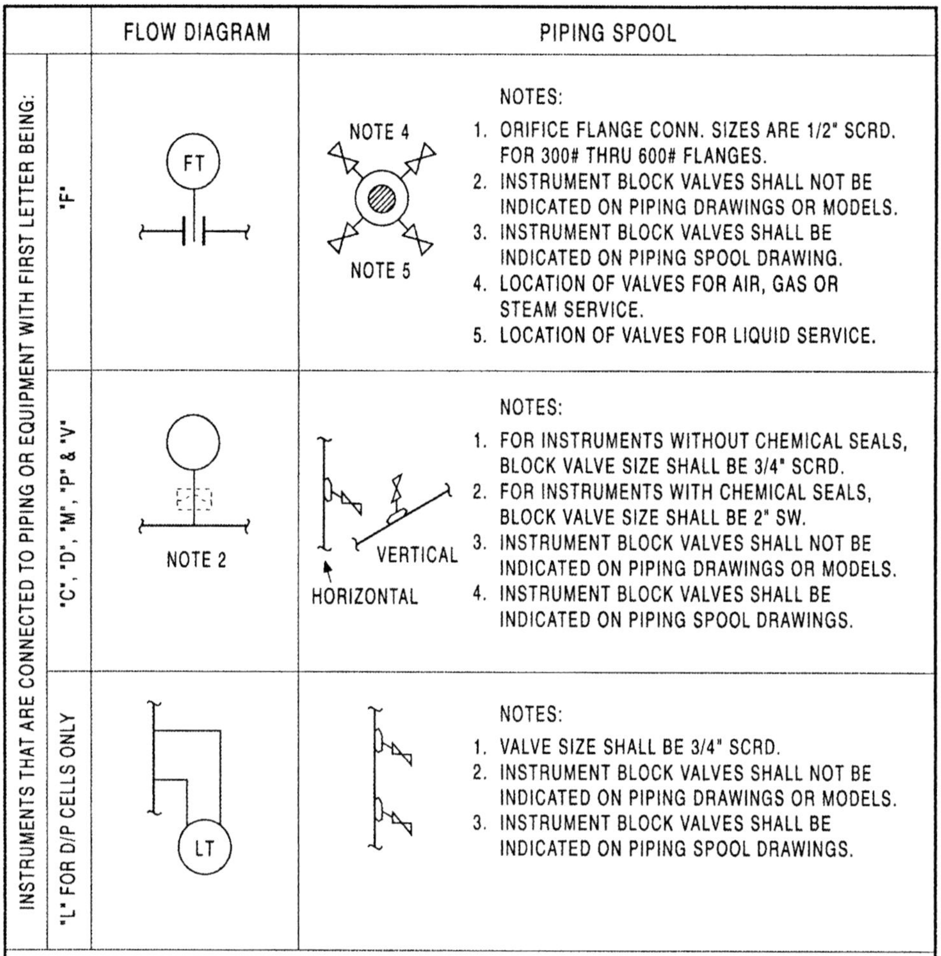

	FLOW DIAGRAM	PIPING SPOOL
"INSTRUMENTS THAT ARE CONNECTED TO PIPING OR EQUIPMENT WITH FIRST LETTER BEING: 'F'"		NOTE 4 / NOTE 5 **NOTES:** 1. ORIFICE FLANGE CONN. SIZES ARE 1/2" SCRD. FOR 300# THRU 600# FLANGES. 2. INSTRUMENT BLOCK VALVES SHALL NOT BE INDICATED ON PIPING DRAWINGS OR MODELS. 3. INSTRUMENT BLOCK VALVES SHALL BE INDICATED ON PIPING SPOOL DRAWING. 4. LOCATION OF VALVES FOR AIR, GAS OR STEAM SERVICE. 5. LOCATION OF VALVES FOR LIQUID SERVICE.
"'C', 'D', 'M', 'P' & 'V'"	NOTE 2	VERTICAL / HORIZONTAL **NOTES:** 1. FOR INSTRUMENTS WITHOUT CHEMICAL SEALS, BLOCK VALVE SIZE SHALL BE 3/4" SCRD. 2. FOR INSTRUMENTS WITH CHEMICAL SEALS, BLOCK VALVE SIZE SHALL BE 2" SW. 3. INSTRUMENT BLOCK VALVES SHALL NOT BE INDICATED ON PIPING DRAWINGS OR MODELS. 4. INSTRUMENT BLOCK VALVES SHALL BE INDICATED ON PIPING SPOOL DRAWINGS.
"'L' FOR D/P CELLS ONLY"		 **NOTES:** 1. VALVE SIZE SHALL BE 3/4" SCRD. 2. INSTRUMENT BLOCK VALVES SHALL NOT BE INDICATED ON PIPING DRAWINGS OR MODELS. 3. INSTRUMENT BLOCK VALVES SHALL BE INDICATED ON PIPING SPOOL DRAWINGS.

EXCEPTIONS

1. INSTRUMENTS SHOWN ON FLOW DIAGRAMS AS "PE" OR "FE" ARE TO HAVE PLUGGED VALVES PER SPECIFICATION:_____.
2. DRAFT INSTRUMENTS DO NOT REQUIRE INSTRUMENT BLOCK VALVES.
3. EXTERNAL DISPLACER LEVEL INSTRUMENTS AND LEVEL GLASSES SHALL HAVE VALVING IN ACCORDANCE WITH SPECIFICATION:_____ AND PIPING STANDARD DRAWING NO.:_____.

FIGURE 10-5
Engineering flow diagram symbols.

Note that the detail does not attempt to give all the information necessary to do the complete installation. For instance, the typical mounting details below the line-mounted instrument detail shown in Figure 10-2 would be necessary to give instructions on how to mount the instrument. Additional details would be necessary for the instrument signal connections. This work breakdown grows out of years of experience and is frequently influenced by the uncertainty of whether the installers will be union or non-union. For instance,

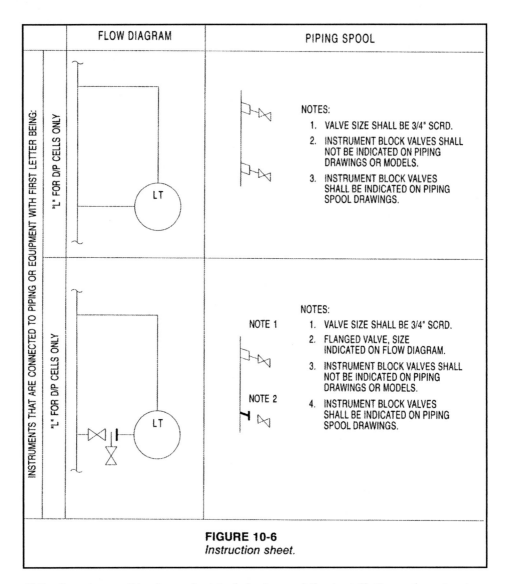

FIGURE 10-6
Instruction sheet.

if the flow transmitter is an electrical device and the installation subcontractor is a union contractor, there will be a potential dispute over who mounts the instrument on the line—the electricians or the pipefitters. If the installation details are sufficiently broken down to match any potential work breakdown, instructions will be given to the right people, regardless of the final resolution of the labor dispute.

The wealth of information carried by a few lines on a drawing is worth re-emphasizing. The arrow on the process pipe ahead of the orifice plate gives the direction of flow. This direction matches the high and low pressure connection notations that are essential for correct connection to the instrument. The orifice connections are to the side, which allows gases to pass over the

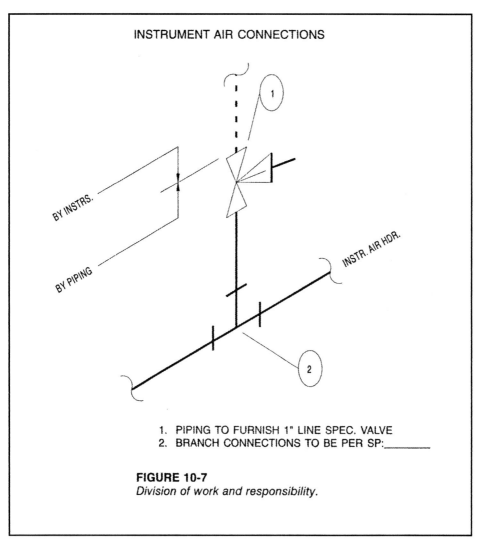

INSTRUMENT AIR CONNECTIONS

1. PIPING TO FURNISH 1" LINE SPEC. VALVE
2. BRANCH CONNECTIONS TO BE PER SP:_____

FIGURE 10-7
Division of work and responsibility.

point of connection and solids to pass under it. The plugged tee connection is a convenient method of rodding out any potential plugging of the orifice taps through the root valves. The slope of the impulse lines is given correctly to permit outgassing on liquid service without the gases collecting at the transmitter and altering its accuracy.

Figure 10-12 is similar to Figure 10-11 but carries an associated bill of materials. It is worth discussing this combination in terms of the style of the drawing and how the bill of materials and the drawing are combined. At one time, the bill of materials was a hand-lettered part of the drawing. With the advent of computerized material takeoffs, it became more convenient to have the bill of materials and the drawing as separate documents. The drawing number references them to one another.

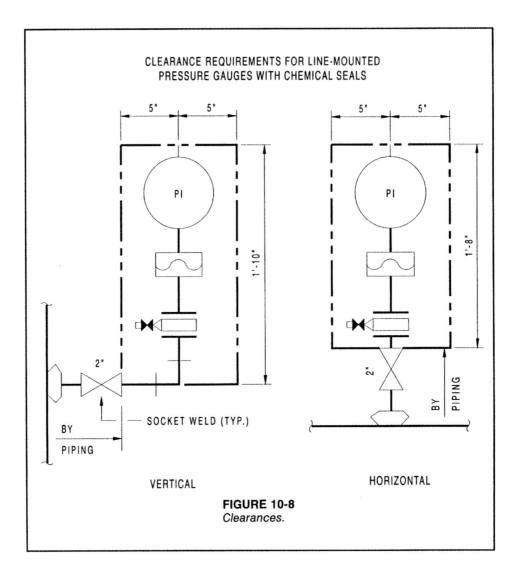

CLEARANCE REQUIREMENTS FOR LINE-MOUNTED
PRESSURE GAUGES WITH CHEMICAL SEALS

FIGURE 10-8
Clearances.

If both the bill of materials and the drawing are produced on 8-1/2 by 11 inch paper, they can easily be reproduced together on an 11 by 17 inch document. Actually, this is really not necessary, especially since the bill of materials becomes a stand-alone document in the hands of a warehouseman. What is required is that the drawing and the bill of materials be associated with each other.

The reader should note the economy of effort involved in the combination. The drawing is very generic, and it could be used over and over again for different specifications. In this case, the material package number carries some specification information: it list, in a very compact format, the essential information necessary for the installation.

CLEARANCE REQUIREMENTS FOR LINE-MOUNTED FLOW TRANSMITTERS (FT)

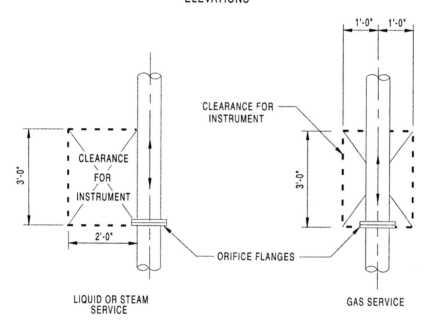

NOTE:
LINE-MOUNTED TRANSMITTERS MAY BE MOUNTED ON EITHER
SIDE OF ORIFICE FLANGES. SEE MODEL FOR ACTUAL LOCATION.

FIGURE 10-9

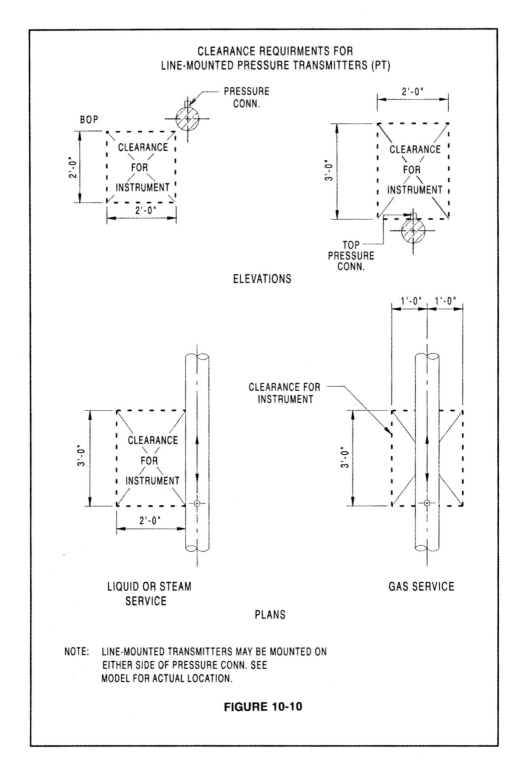

FIGURE 10-10

What is not apparent is that the bill of information is usually computer-generated. An engineer or a technician choosing a standard drawing and matching a material specification furnishes the input data. The computer then not only

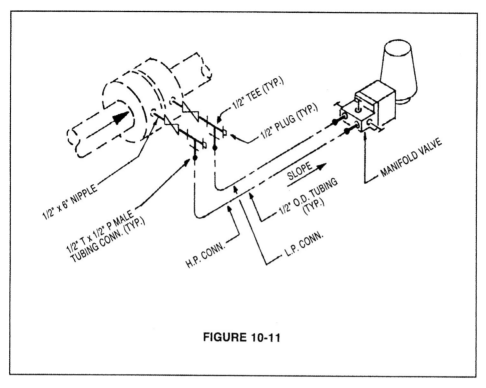

FIGURE 10-11

generates a specific bill of materials, but also adds the information to the data bank so that the material may be purchased in bulk quantities and shipped to the right place at the right time.

Figure 10-13 is another example that typifies good drawing practice. The symbols are very simple. There is no excess information, but there is enough information so that the reader does not need an encyclopedic memory in order to make use of the symbolism. Evidently, this is an instructional drawing. Four separate installation details would be generated from this one drawing.

Figure 10-14 is an example of an orthographic drawing, which shows why an isometric drawing is most often the superior type. It is necessary to show a plan and an elevation on an orthographic drawing, and it is necessary to go through some degree of mental gymnastics to complete the missing parts of the puzzle. Nevertheless, both types are used and both must be understood.

Pressure Instruments

Figure 10-15 shows three installation details that typify pressure instrument connection problems. Again, the drawings must be interpreted according to the legend sheet. The draft gage connection detail shows that care must be taken to permit inspection and cleaning and that consideration must be given

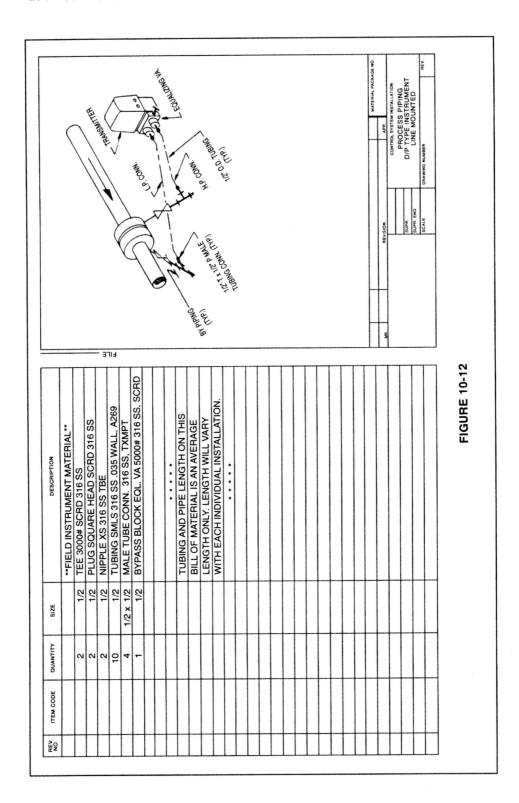

FIGURE 10-12

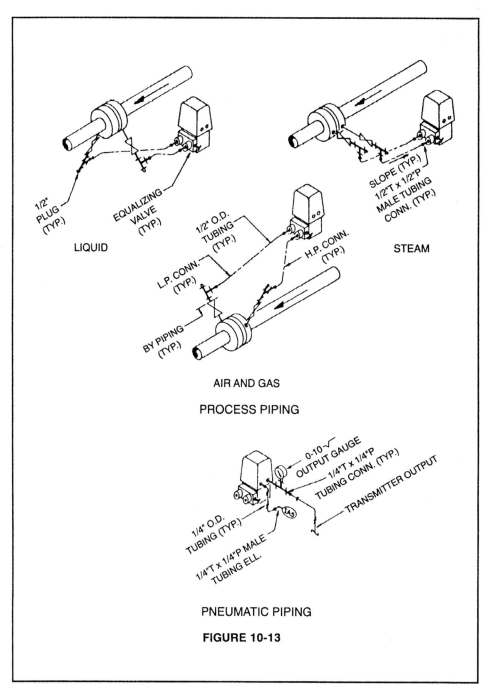

LIQUID

STEAM

AIR AND GAS

PROCESS PIPING

PNEUMATIC PIPING

FIGURE 10-13

to the possibility of condensation. The piped portion of the assembly accomplishes all of this. The tubed portion of the assembly is relatively trouble-free and is treated as capable of being handled by tubing.

Pressure gages are usually presented together on a single sheet and referred to by detail number. The detail is referenced in the Instrument Index. Figure 10-16

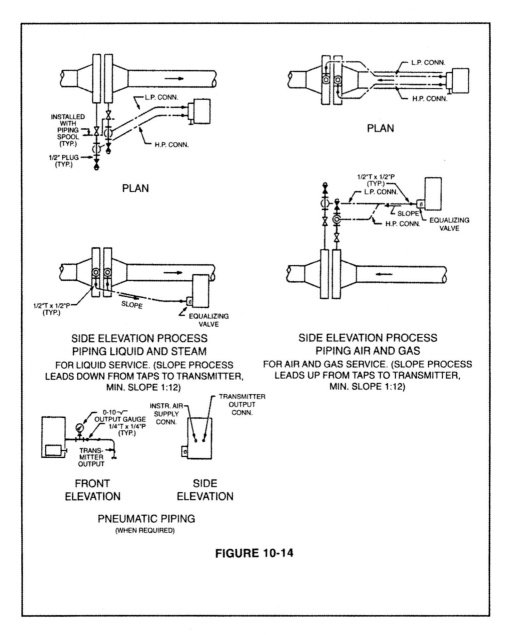

FIGURE 10-14

contains a series of examples and gives instructions as to their use. Do not be misled into thinking that the installer has the freedom to choose which detail will be used. This choice is the responsibility of the engineer. The Instrument Index defines the detail to be used in each specific case.

Level Instruments

Installation details for level instruments are frequently taken from an engineering standard that defines the general approach to the most common installations. The choice of the detail requires cooperation and coordination

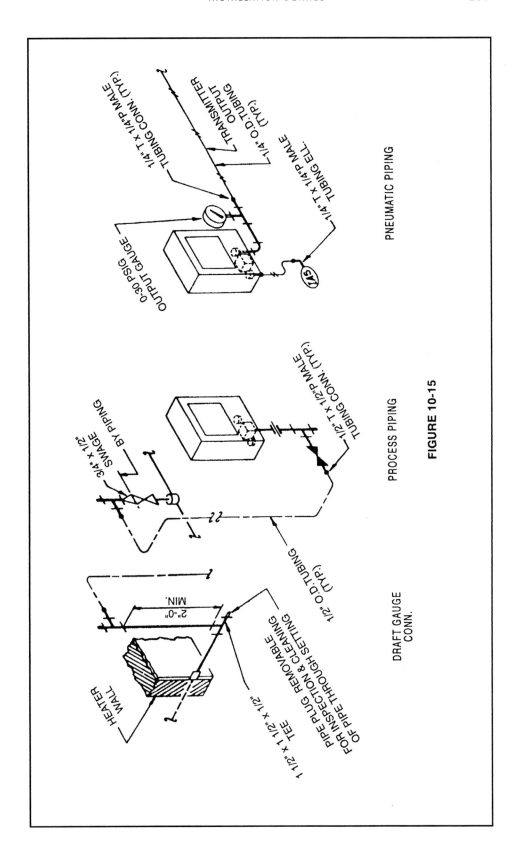

PNEUMATIC PIPING

PROCESS PIPING

DRAFT GAUGE
CONN.

FIGURE 10-15

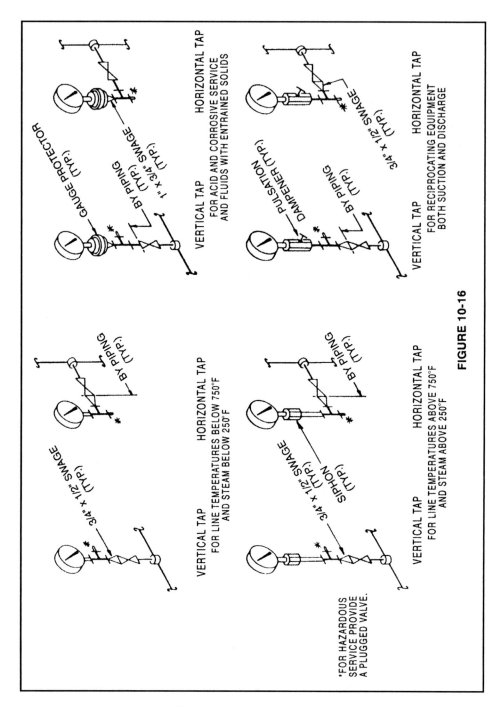

FIGURE 10-16

among process, piping, and instrument personnel. The final detail must define exactly what is to be installed and what the clearances are.

A number of choices are required, depending upon the application. If the vessel is a horizontal one, a bridle is usually used. If it is vertical, there is no bridle. Usually, it is necessary to see the liquid level or interface, so level glasses

LEVEL GLASS AND MAXIMUM D/P CELL RANGE TABLE

	MAXIMUM D/P RANGE	VISIBLE GLASS	NO. OF SECTIONS	℄ TO ℄ CPLG			"K" DIM.
				G1	G2	G3	
TYPE I	23"	25 1/4"	2	33"	–	–	33"
TYPE I	37"	38 5/8"	3	47"	–	–	47"
TYPE I	50"	52"	4	60"	–	–	60"
TYPE II	61"	63"	2 / 3	–	33"	47"	71"
TYPE II	75"	77"	3 / 3	–	47"	47"	85"
TYPE II	88"	90"	3 / 4	–	47"	60"	98"
TYPE II	101"	103"	4 / 4	–	60"	60"	111"
TYPE III	113"	115"	3 / 3 / 3	–	47"	47"	123"
TYPE III	126"	128"	3 / 4 / 3	–	60"	47"	136"
TYPE III	139"	141"	4 / 3 / 4	–	47"	60"	149"
TYPE III	152"	154"	4 / 4 / 4	–	60"	60"	162"

LEGEND: 4 / 4 / 4 THREE LEVEL GLASS ASSEMBLIES OF FOUR GLASS SECTIONS EACH.

GENERAL NOTES

1. BRIDLES WILL NOT BE USED ON VERTICAL VESSELS.
2. BRIDLES WILL NOT BE USED IN CRYOGENIC SERVICE. (-21 F AND BELOW)
3. DIFFERENTIAL PRESSURE TYPE LEVEL INSTRUMENTS WILL NORMALLY BE USED FOR ALL SERVICES EXCEPT:
   3.1 LIQUID-LIQUID INTERFACE SERVICE
   3.2 LEVEL RANGES 14 INCHES OR LESS
4. PIPING MATERIAL WILL BE PER THE PIPING MATERIAL SPECIFICATION.
5. LEVEL GLASS, D/P CELL, AND DISPLACER TYPE LEVEL CONTROLLER PIPING ON THIS DRAWING IS BASED ON LINE CLASSES 150# THRU 600# FLANGED OR SOCKET-WELD CONSTRUCTION.
6. 900# AND GREATER, HYDROGEN, AND CRYOGENIC PIPING SHALL BE DEVELOPED AS REQUIRED FOR CONTRACT USE.
7. THE LEVEL GLASS TABLE DIMENSIONS ARE BASED ON JERGUSON SERIES 20, NUMBER 8 GLASS.

FIGURE 10-17

in various combinations are necessary. A choice of the type of instrument is also made: D/P cell, displacement, capacitance, radiation, etc.

Figure 10-17 shows the general notes associated with a typical engineering standard for level instruments. These notes define when to use bridles, how to make the choice between a D/P cell and a displacer, which piping specification to use, and even the manufacturer (for standardization).

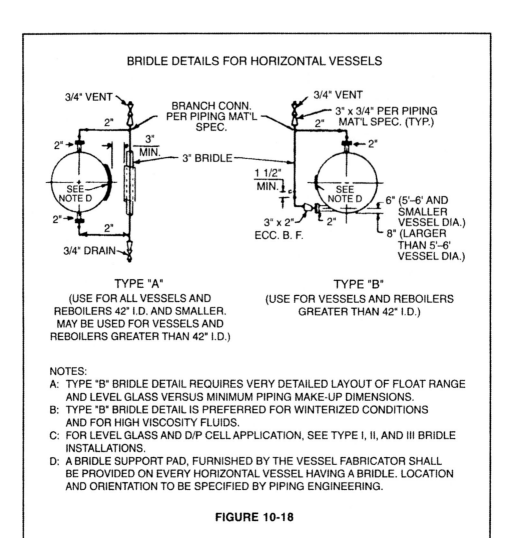

BRIDLE DETAILS FOR HORIZONTAL VESSELS

TYPE "A"
(USE FOR ALL VESSELS AND
REBOILERS 42" I.D. AND SMALLER.
MAY BE USED FOR VESSELS AND
REBOILERS GREATER THAN 42" I.D.)

TYPE "B"
(USE FOR VESSELS AND REBOILERS
GREATER THAN 42" I.D.)

NOTES:
A: TYPE "B" BRIDLE DETAIL REQUIRES VERY DETAILED LAYOUT OF FLOAT RANGE
AND LEVEL GLASS VERSUS MINIMUM PIPING MAKE-UP DIMENSIONS.
B: TYPE "B" BRIDLE DETAIL IS PREFERRED FOR WINTERIZED CONDITIONS
AND FOR HIGH VISCOSITY FLUIDS.
C: FOR LEVEL GLASS AND D/P CELL APPLICATION, SEE TYPE I, II, AND III BRIDLE
INSTALLATIONS.
D: A BRIDLE SUPPORT PAD, FURNISHED BY THE VESSEL FABRICATOR SHALL
BE PROVIDED ON EVERY HORIZONTAL VESSEL HAVING A BRIDLE. LOCATION
AND ORIENTATION TO BE SPECIFIED BY PIPING ENGINEERING.

FIGURE 10-18

Also on the figure is a table that shows the combinations of glasses necessary for various D/P cell ranges. For instance, a type I installation (single glass) with a range of 23 inches will have a visible glass dimension of 25-1/4 inches. It will consist of two sections. The overall dimension between couplings or nozzles will be 33 inches. This table will be used with the figures that follow.

Figure 10-18 gives bridle details for horizontal vessels and divides them into two types, A and B, depending on vessel size. The notes give the reasons for preferences. Installation types I, II, and III referred to in the figure are defined in Figure 10-19 as being one, two, or three "glasses." A glass is defined by its having upper and lower connections; it may consist of several sections, as seen in the table of Figure 10-17.

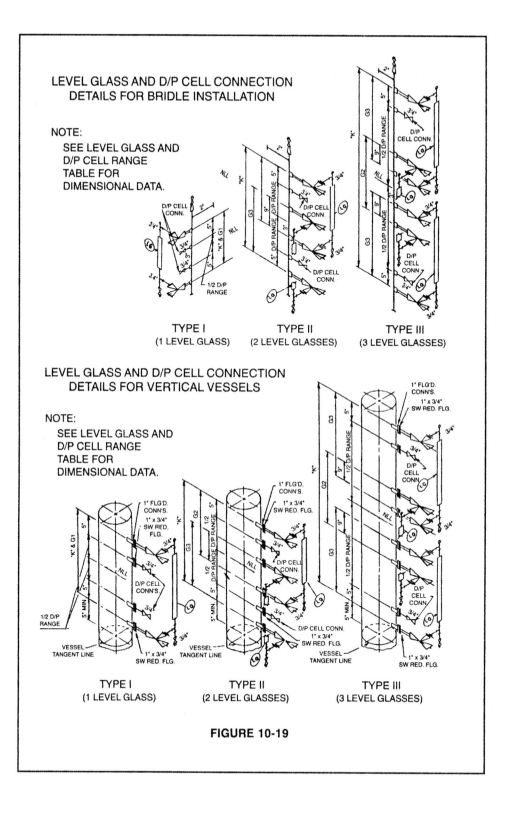

FIGURE 10-19

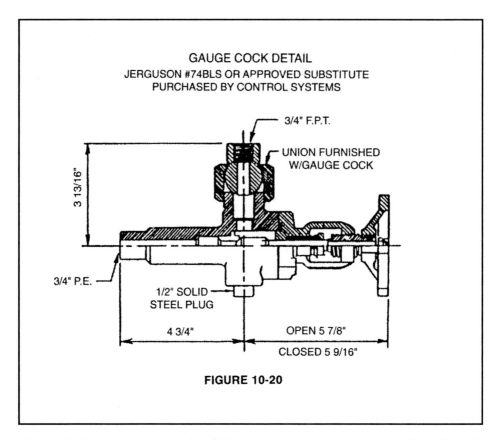

GAUGE COCK DETAIL
JERGUSON #74BLS OR APPROVED SUBSTITUTE
PURCHASED BY CONTROL SYSTEMS

3/4" F.P.T.

UNION FURNISHED
W/GAUGE COCK

3 13/16"

3/4" P.E.

1/2" SOLID
STEEL PLUG

4 3/4"

OPEN 5 7/8"

CLOSED 5 9/16"

FIGURE 10-20

Figure 10-19 is a good example of the thought processes that must be followed in designing the installation. Notice the continuation symbol (the wavy line at the bottom of the bridle) that allows the drawing to be used with either the type A or type B bridles of Figure 10-18. This is the first choice to be made. NLL stands for normal liquid level.

The maximum D/P cell range will fix the installation type (one, two, or three glasses) and all subsequent dimensions. The choice of level and range requires cooperation between the process engineer and the instrument engineer.

The combination of the typical details of Figure 10-19 with the general notes and type and dimension table of Figure 10-17 permits relatively expeditious choices to be made in the majority of applications. The details are a little more complicated than those in previous figures, but they contain a wealth of information in a very simple form. The reader will excuse the author for belaboring this point, but that is what symbols and identification are all about.

Figure 10-20 is a gage cock detail. The union connection permits the accommodation of minor misalignments. This union is shown symbolically on the

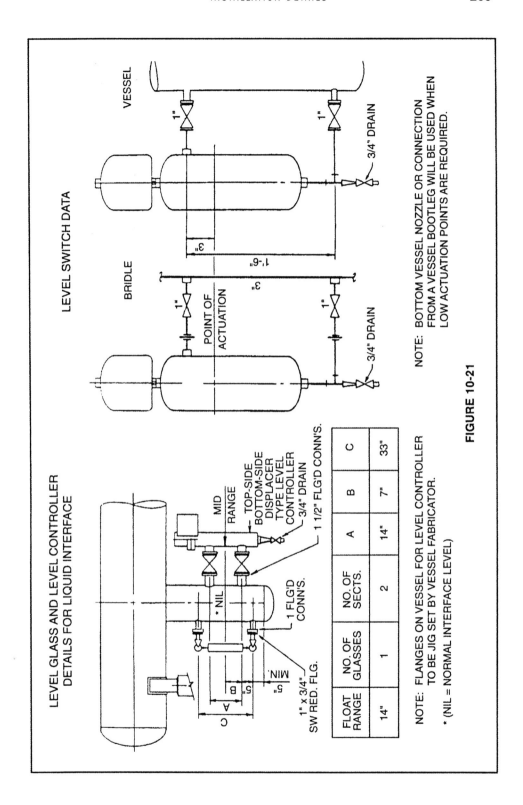

FIGURE 10-21

isometric drawing of Figure 10-19. It connects the valve to the nipple and tee combination on the gage glass.

Level glass and D/P cell connection details for vertical vessels are shown in Figure 10-19. It is to be noted that the bridle is missing and that more nozzles are necessary on the vessel. Depending on cost and convenience, sometimes a decision is made to put a bridle on a vertical vessel.

Figure 10-19 is another example of the wealth of detail that can be described by an isometric drawing. It is also a good example of how it is necessary to combine general notes, a cell range table, a gage cock detail, and an Instrument Index to obtain the complete picture.

Figure 10-21 is another example of an orthographic drawing. The level glass and level controller details for liquid interface are a typical example of an oil-water separator or other liquid interface control problem. The figure also shows how a commonly recurring problem can be standardized once it has been identified.

Similarly, level switches are a fairly common application, and the detail for the level switch is given in the same figure. Again, the two types of installation are given for horizontal (bridle) and vertical vessels.

Miscellaneous Instruments

It is possible to continue categorizing the various types on installation details, but this would become very repetitive. Once the basic principles of work breakdown, choice of format, and simplicity are grasped, it is a fairly straight-forward procedure to begin to build up a library of typical drawings. This library can then be used to create new instrument details, which usually requires only minor adaptations.

This chapter will, therefore, close with a few examples chosen because the authors find them aesthetically or intellectually pleasing.

▨ EXAMPLES

Figure 10-22 shows the process piping (a capillary) and the pneumatic piping (air supply and signal line) for the same transmitter. These would usually form two separate installation details, for the reasons previously given.

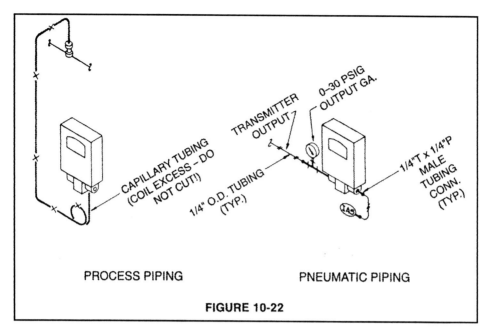

PROCESS PIPING   PNEUMATIC PIPING

FIGURE 10-22

It is interesting to se that the designer feels it necessary to give specific instruc-tions not to cut the capillary. Believe it or not, this is a very important warning. Notice that the pneumatic piping shows by symbolism that a 1/4-inch nipple and tee, an output gage, and three 1/4-inch tube by 1/4-inch male pipe con-nectors are necessary, along with some 1/4-inch tubing. The details will be spelled out on the Bill of Materials.

The instrument air supply (IAS) is frequently depicted symbolically. Figure 10-23 gives three examples of instrument air supplies. The Instrument Index would indicate which one to use.

Figure 10-24 is an example of a differential pressure instrument used for a closed-tank installation together with the detail used for the pneumatic pip-ing. The figure gives some alternative installation possibilities. Only one possi-bility would be chosen for a particular application.

Figure 10-25 shows two examples of purging impulse lines. Again, only one would be used for a particular installation.

Fabrication drawings are closely related to installation details and are frequently given the same format. Figure 10-26 is an example of a standard 3/4-inch screwed thermowell fabrication detail. It would be accompanied by design notes and construction notes that indicate materials of construction, hydrostatic test-ing requirements, and stamping requirements (303 SS, 316 SS, A 20, M, CS, etc.).

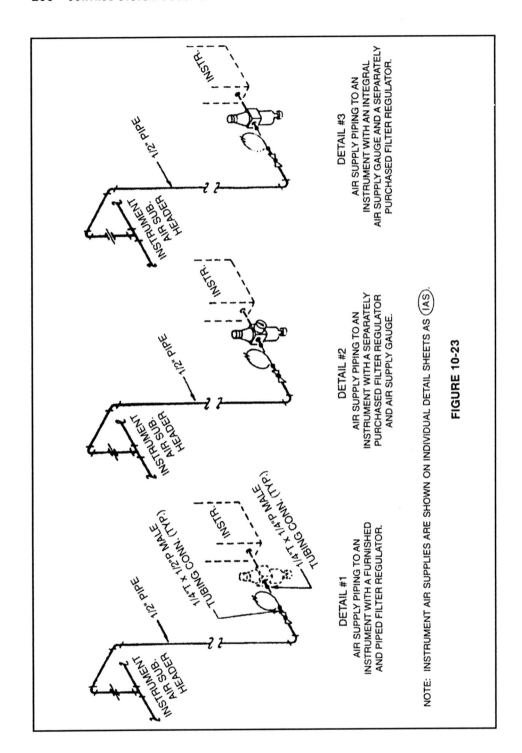

DETAIL #1

AIR SUPPLY PIPING TO AN
INSTRUMENT WITH A FURNISHED
AND PIPED FILTER REGULATOR.

DETAIL #2

AIR SUPPLY PIPING TO AN
INSTRUMENT WITH A SEPARATELY
PURCHASED FILTER REGULATOR
AND AIR SUPPLY GAUGE.

DETAIL #3

AIR SUPPLY PIPING TO AN
INSTRUMENT WITH AN INTEGRAL
AIR SUPPLY GAUGE AND A SEPARATELY
PURCHASED FILTER REGULATOR.

NOTE: INSTRUMENT AIR SUPPLIES ARE SHOWN ON INDIVIDUAL DETAIL SHEETS AS (IAS).

FIGURE 10-23

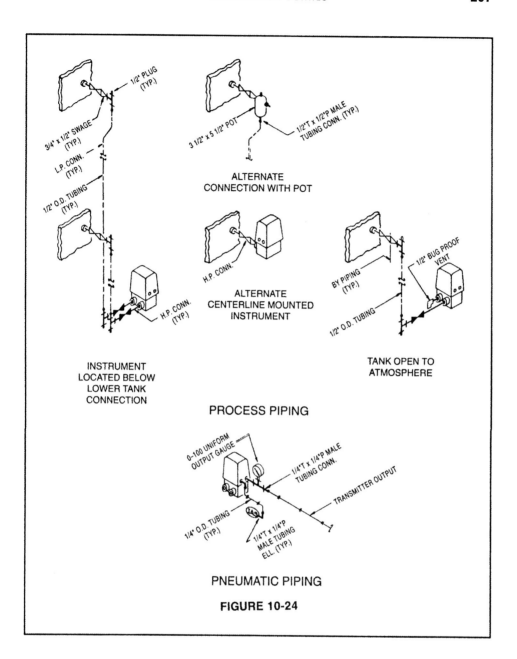

FIGURE 10-24

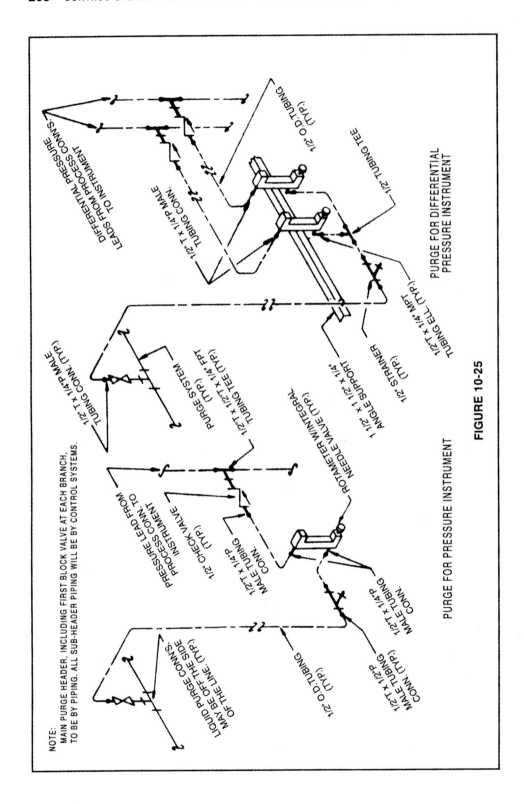

FIGURE 10-25

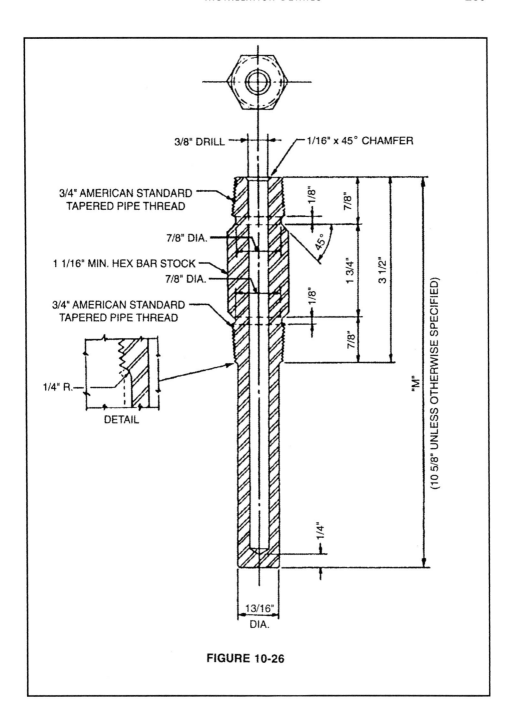

FIGURE 10-26

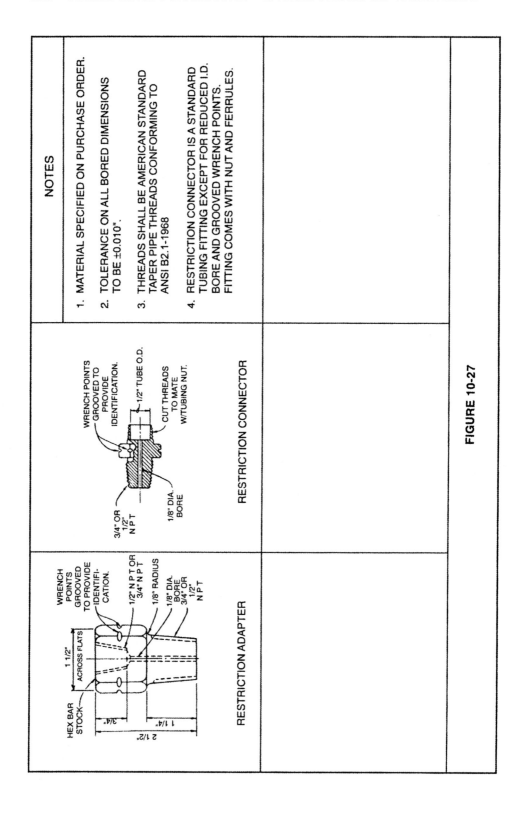

NOTES

1. MATERIAL SPECIFIED ON PURCHASE ORDER.

2. TOLERANCE ON ALL BORED DIMENSIONS TO BE ±0.010".

3. THREADS SHALL BE AMERICAN STANDARD TAPER PIPE THREADS CONFORMING TO ANSI B2.1-1968

4. RESTRICTION CONNECTOR IS A STANDARD TUBING FITTING EXCEPT FOR REDUCED I.D. BORE AND GROOVED WRENCH POINTS. FITTING COMES WITH NUT AND FERRULES.

RESTRICTION CONNECTOR

RESTRICTION ADAPTER

FIGURE 10-27

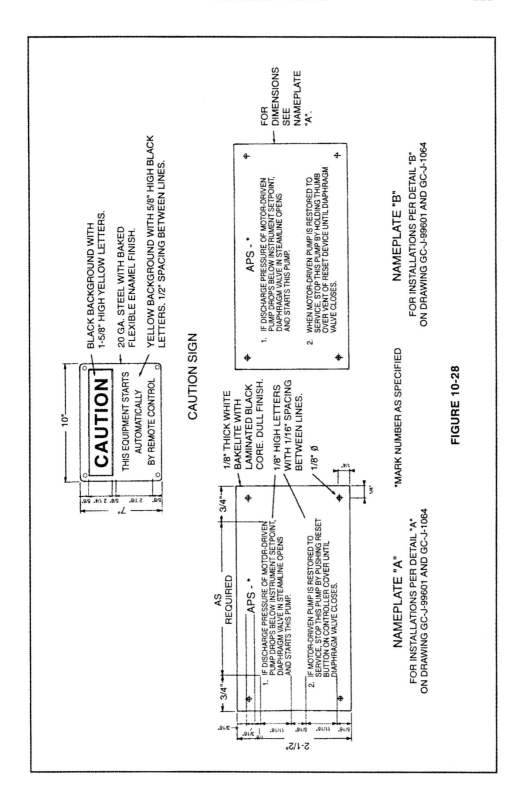

FIGURE 10-28

Figure 10-27 shows the seemingly minor but important details with which instrument designers and engineers are involved. Figure 10-28 was chosen to remind the reader that the exhortation to medical doctors to do as little harm as possible also applies to instrument and controls personnel.

SUMMARY

The chapter starts out with a definition of what instrument details and the associated fabrication details are: a specific instruction to someone to fabricate or install a particular instrument. It goes on to show that the drawing is usually limited to a specific task. For instance, separate drawings would be made for instrument mounting, instrument process connections, and instrument piping or electrical connections.

The drawing size is discussed, and the reader is warned not to use drawings any bigger than 11 by 17 inches (or their metric equivalents). An exception to this rule would be when the drawings form part of a standard meant for guidance and instruction. The reason for the rule is that the installer has enough equipment to worry about without carrying a full-sized drawing around.

The separation of the installation detail and the bill of materials is discussed. It has become commonplace for a computer to be used to generate bills of materials.

Finally, many examples of typical installation details are given. It should not be construed that every possible detail is covered. The word "library" is used deliberately in connection with installation details. Most designers and engineers will build up quite an extensive library of such drawings in the course of their careers.

QUESTIONS

1. What is the function of an instrument installation detail?
2. What document is integrally associated with the installation detail?
3. What two formats are given as standard for the installation detail?
4. What two styles of installation detail are given as standard? What are their uses?
5. What four typical steps does an installation subcontractor follow when installing an instrument?

6. Can you see that each type of instruction document is important in its own right?

7. Why is it important for a firm (or an individual) to build up a library of typical installation details?

8. Why should a designer or engineer modify his approach to drawing format and contents because a union might be involved in the installation?

11

MISCELLANEOUS DRAWINGS

▨ INTRODUCTION: THE REMAINING WORK

The remaining work to round out the coverage of applied instrumentation and identification includes control panel drawings and location plans. Neither subject is sufficiently broad to warrant its own chapter, so both will be grouped under the heading, "Miscellaneous Drawings."

▨ CONTROL PANELS

Control panels are usually divided into two major categories: local and remote. "Local" refers to proximity to the process. "Remote" refers to remoteness from the process. "Remote" is synonymous with "central" when the word "central" is used to mean centralized, i.e., when signals from all over the plant are brought to a centralized location.

Local panels frequently must be built to withstand harsher environments than central ones. They may be exposed not only to the industrial environment but also to washdown practices, rain, sleet, snow and ice. This fact does not influence drawing style or practices. It is usually covered in the written specification that accompanies the drawings.

Central panels most often are located in control rooms in an air-conditioned environment. They are built to more general-purpose standards.

Keyboards and CRTs, or more correctly today visual display units (VDUs) since non-cathode ray tube displays predominate, have replaced the so-called conventional panels to such a degree that it is difficult to know to which to apply the term "conventional." The so-called shared display is often ruggedized. (Keyboards, especially, must be built to withstand the ravages of spilled coffee and cookie crumbs.)

Distributed control systems consoles allow less artistic license to the engineer than do the more conventional panels, but the engineer still must choose them and arrange them so that the operator may function efficiently. Human engineering is as important as ever.

Local panels are often placed on raised concrete curbs to avoid water penetration into the panel compartment. Central control room panels are often placed on "computer" floors to allow ease of access for wiring.

Purpose of Control Panel

A control panel houses instruments. It is also an interface point between an operator and the process. It must be designed with two ideas in mind.

The first idea is that the operator can have effective control over a process only if he or she can receive and comprehend incoming information and can take appropriate corrective action expeditiously. Therefore, the panel must be designed with an average operator's span of control in mind.

The second idea is that the equipment must be maintained. The maintenance technician must have ready access to the instruments, and the key components must be adaptable to rapid change out and repair.

Evolution

It is interesting to follow the evolution of control panel design history. Early panels simply housed instruments: they kept instruments together in a convenient, protected location. Space being at a premium, they frequently neither satisfied the operator nor the maintenance man; instruments were often crowded and difficult to access.

When it was realized that production time could be lost through poor design, attempts were made to treat the panel face as an operator interface point and the panel rear as a maintenance interface point. When it was further realized that not all instruments required the same frequency of operator attention, recorders and counters were put on vertical panels at the rear of the control room, and controllers and push buttons were placed on consoles at which a seated operator on a swivel chair could more efficiently be in command of the process.

So-called full graphics were an attempt to place instruments within a graphic depiction of the process; for instance, a push button would be placed within a symbol for the actuated device. Full graphics were soon replaced by semi-graphics, which grouped instruments in a logical spatial arrangement below the graphic representation of the process. Here is another case in which words can be misleading to the non-initiated; much more information can be presented on a semi-graphic than on a full graphic.

Before the advent of shared display systems, large plants would have semi-graphic panels that could be many feet long with consoles in front of them. These consoles required several operators to be located along the length because it was physically impossible for one person to see and to reach everything on the panel in an expeditious manner.

With shared display technology, it became possible to switch the graphic displays and to make the fixed keyboard functions correspond to the display shown. One person could then comprehend and control a multiplicity of functions. "Touch screens" have become common, so that we have come full circle on the semi-graphic versus full-graphic argument.

Now the problem is one of operator overload. Shrinking the size of a panel to a single VDU screen is great when the plant is functioning smoothly but what happens when several process units go into an alarm state simultaneously? Obviously, there must be an economic tradeoff among redundancy (in terms of access from more than one console), potential damage to equipment, data concentration, and operator fatigue.

Techniques such as "first out" annunciation which allows the operator to see which were the first alarms, in a chain of alarms can be used. Secondary alarm suppression is sometimes used when multiple events require that the operator concentrate attention only on critical variables.

Maintenance access is the other side of the same coin. Local panels are still subject to the same space constraints as ever, although local instruments are becoming more compact and multiplexed signals do not require so much space. Still, every effort must be made to see that equipment is chosen and located so that it is accessible for maintenance.

National codes usually specify overall safety parameters such as minimum clearance for access. They say little about good design to allow rapid location of the correct device and its terminals. (Neither do they say much about allowing sufficient access to terminal strips with a normal-sized screwdriver to avoid the skinning of knuckles.)

Central control rooms permit more separation between those controls necessary to the operator and those that are not essential to operator access. Behind-the-panel instruments are frequently removed from the main panel and placed in racks in rack rooms that are remote from the operator interface.

Operator-Machine Interface

The human engineering aspects of the interface between the process and the operator are becoming more and more important. In terms of panel design, human engineering means studying the physical and psychological capabilities of average operators and designing and constructing equipment that will permit these operators to function as efficiently as possible.

The average operator may be female or male, tall or short, sound of limb or handicapped. She or he may be tone deaf or partially color blind, or any combination of the above. It does not matter. The problem remains: How does the engineer/designer create an efficient interface?

First, one studies the subjects, the operator, and the interface. Figure 11-1 and Table 11-1 show body dimensions normally associated with instrumentation. Liptak [Ref. 1] recommends that the source of the data be kept in mind (students, soldiers, physicians). A height-adjustable swivel chair on rolers in front of a wraparound console can be used to increase the operator's span of control and must be integrated into such data.

Although the subject of human engineering is very interesting, the primary purpose of this book is to discuss the practical application of symbols and identification. The above material is mentioned in order that the reader not lose sight of the bigger picture into which the study of symbols and identification fits.

General Guidelines

This book is aimed at the practicing engineer/designer; this chapter is meant primarily for the person who wishes to have a panel built to his or her conceptual design. It contains recommendations on the type of drawing used to obtain more general approvals and to give instructions to a panel fabricator.

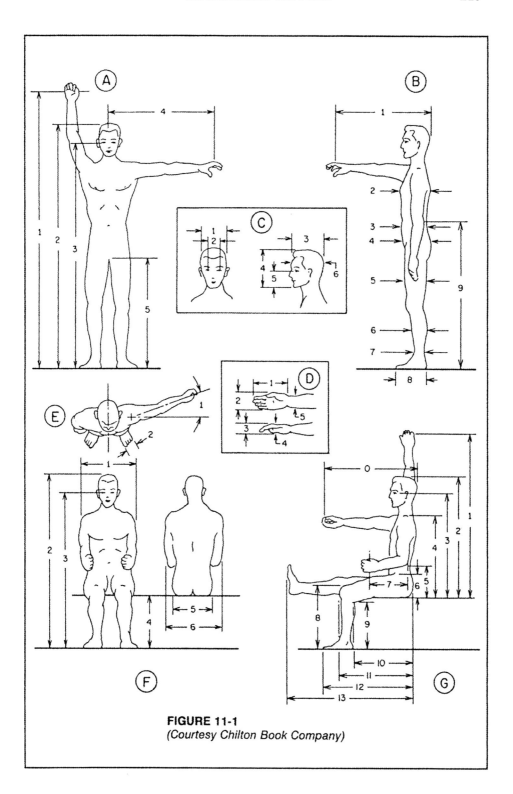

FIGURE 11-1
(Courtesy Chilton Book Company)

Table 11-1
MALE HUMAN BODY DIMENSIONS
Selected dimensions of the human body (ages 18 to 45).
Locations of dimensions correspond to those in Figure 3.5c.

Dimensional Element			Dimension in inches (m) except where noted	
			5th Percentile	95th Percentile
		Weight in pounds (kg)	132 (59.4)	201 (90.5)
A	1	Vertical reach	77.0 (1.9)	89.0 (2.2)
	2	Stature	65.0 (1.6)	73.0 (1.8)
	3	Eye to floor	61.0 (1.5)	69.0 (1.7)
	4	Side arm reach from center line of body	29.0 (0.7)	34.0 (0.8)
	5	Crotch to floor	30.0 (0.75)	36.0 (0.9)
B	1	Forward arm reach	28.0 (0.7)	33.0 (0.8)
	2	Chest circumference	35.0 (0.87)	43.0 (1.1)
	3	Waist circumference	28.0 (0.7)	38.0 (0.95)
	4	Hip circumference	34.0 (0.8)	42.0 (1.1)
	5	Thigh circumference	20.0 (0.5)	25.0 (0.6)
	6	Calf circumference	13.0 (0.3)	16.0 (0.4)
	7	Ankle circumference	8.0 (200 mm)	10.0 (250 mm)
	8	Foot length	9.8 (245 mm)	11.3 (283 mm)
	9	Elbow to floor	41.0 (1.0)	46.0 (1.2)
C	1	Head width	5.7 (143 mm)	6.4 (160 mm)
	2	Interpupillary distance	2.27 (56.75 mm)	2.74 (68.5 mm)
	3	Head length	7.3 (183 mm)	8.2 (205 mm)
	4	Head height	—	10.2 (255 mm)
	5	Chin to eye	—	5.0 (125 mm)
	6	Head circumference	21.5 (0.54)	23.5 (0.59)
D	1	Hand length	6.9 (173 mm)	8.0 (200 mm)
	2	Hand width	3.7 (92.5 mm)	4.4 (110 mm)
	3	Hand thickness	1.05 (26.25 mm)	1.28 (32 mm)
	4	Fist circumference	10.7 (267.5 mm)	12.4 (310 mm)
	5	Wrist circumference	6.3 (39.7 mm)	7.5 (186 mm)
E	1	Arm swing, aft	40 degrees	40 degrees
	2	Foot width	3.5 (87.5 mm)	4.0 (100 mm)
F	1	Shoulder width	17.0 (0.4)	19.0 (0.48)
	2	Sitting height to floor (std chair)	52.0 (1.3)	56.0 (1.4)
	3	Eye to floor (std chair)	47.4 (1.2)	51.5 (1.3)
	4	Standard chair	18.0 (0.45)	18.0 (0.45)
	5	Hip breadth	13.0 (0.3)	15.0 (0.38)
	6	Width between elbows	15.0 (0.38)	20.0 (0.5)
G	0	Arm reach (finger grasp)	30.0 (0.75)	35.0 (0.88)
	1	Vertical reach	45.0 (1.1)	53.0 (1.3)
	2	Head to seat	33.8 (0.84)	38.0 (0.95)
	3	Eye to seat	29.4 (0.7)	33.5 (0.83)
	4	Shoulder to seat	21.0 (0.52)	25.0 (0.6)
	5	Elbow rest	7.0 (175 mm)	11.0 (275 mm)
	6	Thigh clearance	4.8 (120 mm)	6.5 (162 mm)
	7	Forearm length	13.6 (340 mm)	16.2 (405 mm)
	8	Knee clearance to floor	20.0 (0.5)	23.0 (0.58)
	9	Lower leg height	15.7 (393 mm)	18.2 (455 mm)
	10	Seat length	14.8 (370 mm)	21.5 (0.54)
	11	Buttock-knee length	21.9 (0.55)	36.7 (0.92)
	12	Buttock-toe clearance	32.0 (0.8)	37.0 (0.93)
	13	Buttock-foot length	39.0 (0.98)	46.0 (1.2)

Note: All except critical dimensions have been rounded off to the nearest inch (mm).

(Courtesy Chilton Book Company)

The drawings and specifications given the panel fabricator set the constraints within which the detailed design of the panel must be completed. The fabricator's design details are, generally, beyond the scope of this chapter.

Variety of Panel Drawings

The drawings produced generally hinge on the degree of freedom the initial designer wishes or is allowed to give the panel fabricator in the detailed design. They depend also on the standards and procedures required for a particular project.

Sometimes engineers' sketches (see Figure 11-2) are quite adequate to obtain the desired result. At other times the drawings become quite formal and undergo the complete approval/revision cycle before being issued for bid and fabrication. Regardless of the degree of complexity of presentation, the designer must consider and set down the detailed design constraints in a clear and concise manner.

At times it is possible to take advantage of a vendor's standard panel. Figure 11-3 shows some of The Foxboro Company's standard offerings [Ref. 2]. The drawings are included because they show a variety of panels with the essential dimensions and angles. Dimensions are given in inches and millimeters, and a table is included that shows how it is possible to keep drawings unencumbered by too many figures.

Tables also permit one drawing to represent more than one panel. For instance, in Figure 11-3, the top left-hand drawing represents both a 66-inch console and a 58-inch console (a look over console). The left and center drawings at the bottom represent cabinets with sloped faces in a similar fashion. It is to be noted that the console is not a sit-down model. Its purpose is to make more panel face and, therefore, more instruments available to the standing operator. Compare the sum of the C dimension and 20.1 inches on Model 8371 with the E dimension on Model 8373-D—47.2 inches versus 37.1 inches. This is one example of human engineering. The operator would have difficulty reaching an extra row of instruments on a vertical panel.

Other examples of human engineering are the angles given the front of the panel, the console bench board, and the top sections of the panel. The latter section is for semi-graphic displays or for annunciators.

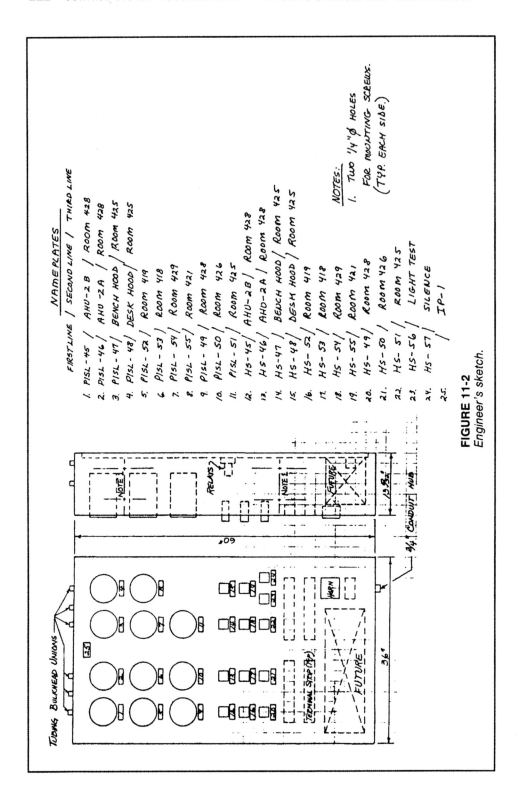

FIGURE 11-2
Engineer's sketch.

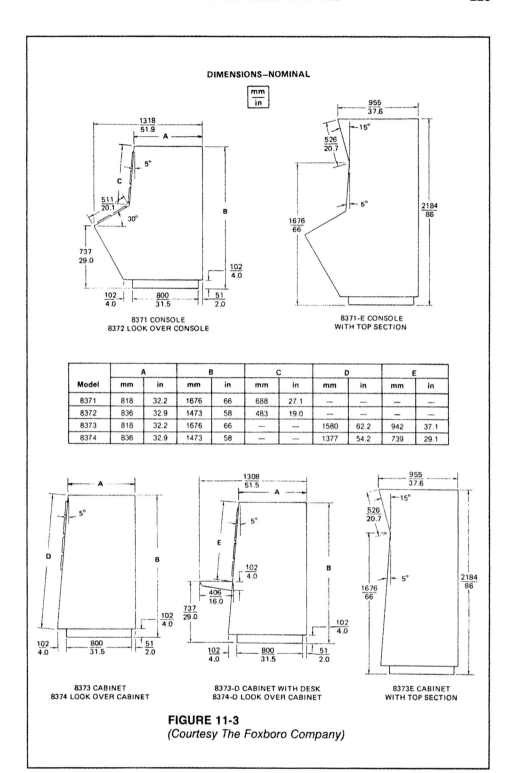

Model	A		B		C		D		E	
	mm	in	mm	in	mm	in	mm	in	mm	in
8371	818	32.2	1676	66	688	27.1	—	—	—	—
8372	836	32.9	1473	58	483	19.0	—	—	—	—
8373	818	32.2	1676	66	—	—	1580	62.2	942	37.1
8374	836	32.9	1473	58	—	—	1377	54.2	739	29.1

FIGURE 11-3
(Courtesy The Foxboro Company)

Typical Central Control Room Panel Drawings

A typical central control room panel drawing will include more information than is needed by the panel fabricator for fabrication of the panel. For instance, it will usually show a small plan view of the control room itself to give the overall orientation and the clearances for access and for the swing radius of doors.

The drawing usually shows a plan, front elevation, and one or two sections and contains the following information:

1. The overall height, length and depth dimensions
2. The instrument location and centerline dimensions
3. Nameplate locations and inscriptions (usually in a reference number/table form)
4. Access door locations, sizes, and swing clearances
5. Curb, computer floor, platform, or concrete pad details
6. Terminal strip locations with typical clearances and wiring routing methods
7. Conduit, cable, and tubing entry locations and methods
8. Other details regarding such items as duct banks and air supplies

The essential information usually is transmitted to the fabricator on a single drawing. The drawing defines the locations and dimensions that the designer wishes to fix but still leaves the fabricator a certain freedom of choice as to detailed design features.

Often, it is difficult to decide what information to put on a drawing and what to put on a specification. Architectural and engineering firms (A&E) tend toward putting all information on drawings, while engineering and construction firms (E&C) and operating companies more often combine a specification with a drawing. In the latter case, the golden rule (do not put a single piece of information in more than one place) should be remembered.

Some information lends itself to the written word (specification) and some is transmitted more meaningfully by symbols (drawing). For instance, material specifications (8-gage panel fronts, 12-gage general structure, 16-gage access doors), paint specifications (polyurethane, so many mils, so many coats), fabrication detail instructions, and crating instructions are all better handled on a specification. A drawing is worth a thousand words when it comes to relative locations, dimensions, relative sizes, and shapes. In suggesting without detailing, the reader needs to use his or her own imagination and know how to complete the details of the picture.

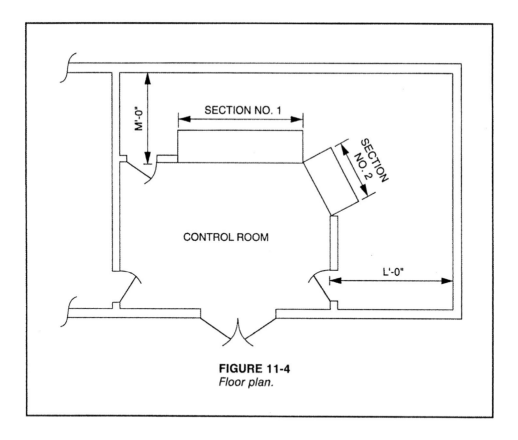

FIGURE 11-4
Floor plan.

Figures 11-4 and 1-5 are drawings that were made for instructional purposes. They represent a hypothetical central control room and would normally appear on one drawing together with many design details.

The floor plan, Figure 11-4, gives an idea of how to show the location of specific sections, clearances, and means of ingress and egress. Figure 11-5 is the front elevation of Section No. 1 of the plan. It shows how to specify center locations of panel cutouts, leaving exact cutout dimensions to the fabricator to obtain from the certified drawings associated with the instrument. If the drawing is to be repeated with only minor changes to dimensions, the dimensions are given a letter code and the numbers are given in tabular form.

Typically, a tag number identifies the locations of specific instruments, while nameplates are coded numerically and tabulated separately. A cross identifies blank instrument locations. Behind-the-panel equipment is shown dashed, when necessary, to depict relative locations. The semi-graphic location is shown in outline only. It requires a larger scale drawing to show it fully, so the reference is given.

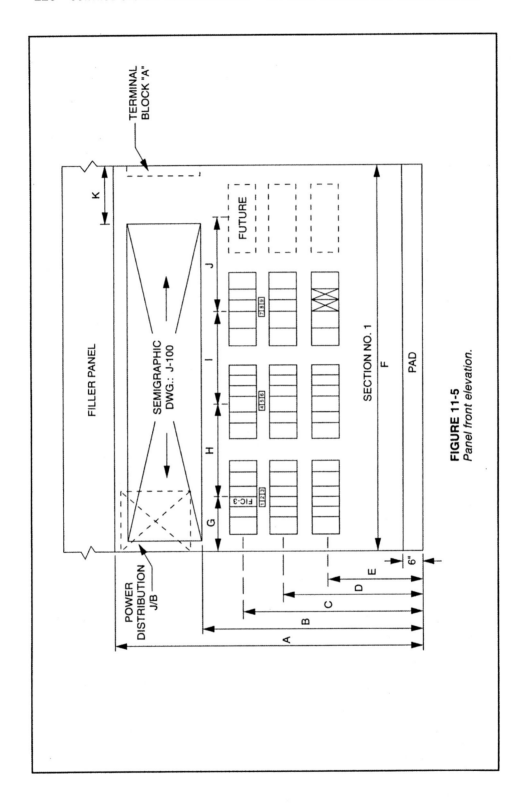

FIGURE 11-5
Panel front elevation.

Semi-Graphics

The semi-graphic section of Figure 11-5 is usually accompanied by a series of full-sized Mylar™ drawings. Figure 11-6 represents one of these drawings. The drawings are frequently color coded and mounted on egg crate matrices so that valve operator lights and alarm lights may be directly located behind the associated symbols. The beauty of this approach is that changes to the process or the process control scheme are easily accommodated. The Mylars are easily revised, and the alarm/pilot lights are easily relocated. Also, a supervisor entering a control room can get a quick, overall grasp of the health of the plant simply by scanning the entire semi-graphic display from left to right.

Visual Display Units

Visual Display units (VDUs) are more and more commonly used. The advantage of VDUs is that many different process displays, including tabular alarm summaries and graphs based on calculated data, may be called up. Colors, blinking, and different intensities of light may be used to great advantage.

The disadvantage is the size of a single VDU display when compared with a semi-graphic display. It is difficult to get an overall grasp of the total plant from a single VDU display. The designer must exercise great ingenuity in creating meaningful displays within the confines of the VDU.

▓ LOCATION PLANS

Instrument location drawings are intended to give instructions to construction personnel about where to install instruments, nothing more. The "how" is left to other drawings.

Since location drawings are usually plan drawings that are dedicated to the installation of instruments, they are also convenient drawings upon which to show conduit, cable, and sometimes even air header routing to the same instruments.

When a good, detailed model (stick-built or 3-D graphics) exists, the location drawing is not required. Frequently, not all parts of a plant will be modeled, so it becomes necessary to have a combination of drawings and model sections that show instrument locations. It goes without saying that the instrument index must also carry the location drawing number or the model section number. The index is the starting point in any information search regarding a particular instrument.

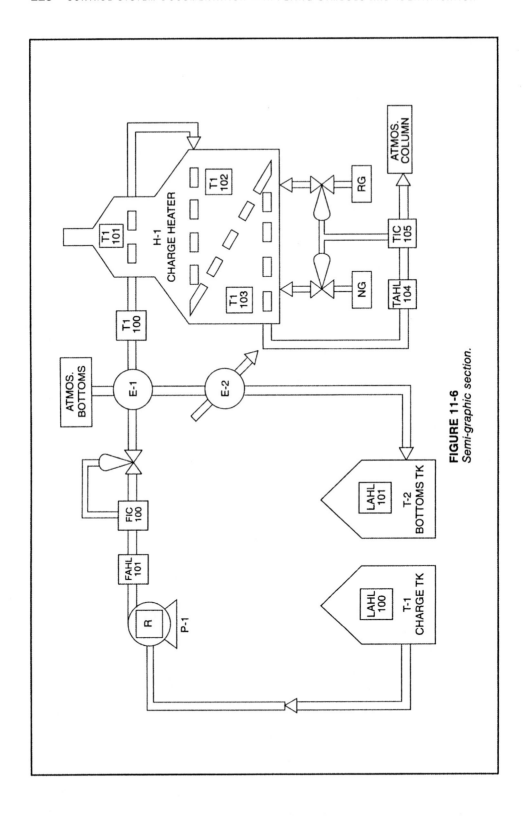

FIGURE 11-6
Semi-graphic section.

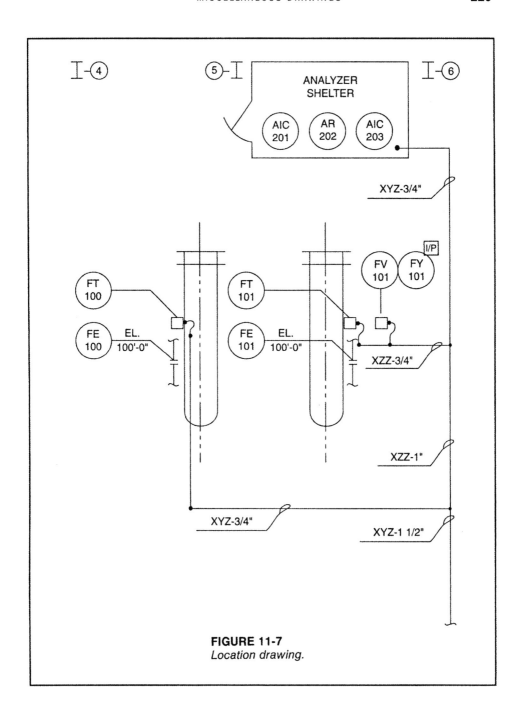

FIGURE 11-7
Location drawing.

The instrument location drawing is usually a plan drawing. Figure 11-7 is a small section of such a drawing. The location drawing often uses as a background a piping layout drawing from which non-essential details have been removed. It then adds the instrument flags (circles containing the tag number) together with leader lines pointing to the exact location of the instrument.

When the elevation of the instrument differs substantially from the general elevation of four and a half feet above platform height, it is called out beside the instrument flag. FE-100 close to Exchanger E-200 and FE-101 near E-201 are cases in point.

The one instrument that is frequently not shown on an instrument location plan is the simple pressure gage. The reason is that its connection to piping will be found on a piping drawing, and it is more convenient to refer to the piping drawing for the location of pressure gages.

The location drawing shows the physical locations of instruments, junction boxes, instrument cabinets, panels, and shelters. It also shows the routing of conduit, cables, and cable tray from the instrument, junction box, cabinet, panel, or shelter to the drawing limit.

The instrument location plan is usually the last instrumentation drawing made on a project. When the drawing is being produced is also the last time that the designer will have a chance to check the clearances and accessibility of the device being located.

Backchecking is a very important engineering function. With so many instrumentation details that can slip through cracks, backchecking the location plan and its cross-referenced documents is the last chance for the engineer and designer to control the quality of their ultimate product, the plant.

▓ SUMMARY

This chapter has discussed control panel drawings and location plans. It has tried to give some guidelines to the instrument engineer or designer regarding the operator-machine interface and the importance of setting constraints on the panel designer without unnecessarily limiting his or her ability to be innovative in the design details.

Throughout this chapter, and this book, it has been stressed that the audience for a particular drawing or specification must be kept in mind. Sometimes there is more than one audience, for instance, the panel fabricator and the installation subcontractor. A means must be found to get the right instructions to the right audience (usually by words on a drawing or in a specification).

The location drawing was discussed and its primary purpose (for the installation contractor to locate the instrument) given. The fact that it is a convenient document to use for the routing of instrument piping, tubing, and signal cables was also mentioned.

Finally, the all important backchecking function was stressed, and mention was made that this document is the last chance for final quality control on the instrument engineer's and instrument designer's product—a working plant.

▨ QUESTIONS

1. What are the two prime functions of a control panel?

2. When talking of panels, how are the words 'local' and 'remote' applied? What word is synonymous with remote?

3. Go over the historical evolution of control panels to establish in your own mind that change is a natural process

4. What is meant by 'human engineering'? Can you think of examples of bad human engineering?

5. Are the drawings and specifications given a panel fabricator by an engineering contractor suitable for final fabrication? If not, why not? Explain the differences between these drawing and final drawings.

6. What are the differences in approach taken by an A&E firm and an E&C firm regarding panel drawings?

7. The words 'information overload' and 'human engineering' suggest that there is more involved in panel design than simply finding a place to locate instruments and functions. Think about this subject and see if you cannot improve upon standard approaches.

REFERENCE
1. Liptak, G. Bela, 1969, 1985, 1995. *Instrument Engineers' Handbook: Process Control.* Third Edition. Radnor, PA: Chilton Book Company.
2. Foxboro Greenbook, Panel Drawings, Foxboro, MA: Foxboro Company.